Dedicated to Missouri Voluntary 4-H Leaders

FIFTY YEARS of 4-H
IN MISSOURI

1914 - 1964

....a unique experience in
youth education

Clyde H. Duncan

Background research and photographs provided by

Robert S. Clough

Publication Supported by a Missouri 4-H Foundation Grant
in cooperation with
University of Missouri Extension Division

Library of Congress Card Catalog Number: 79-629342

Table of Contents

Introduction

by Frank Graham, Director
Extension Youth Programs

In the epic period between 1914 and 1964, agriculture came of age. By 1914 the colleges of agriculture, and their research arms, the state experiment stations, had already begun to serve the needs of a great and growing nation. As the State of Missouri and the nation grew, there was a pressing demand for more feed and more food. This demand led to an agricultural renaissance, and this makes the 50 years between 1914 and 1964 one of the most significant and interesting periods in the history of Missouri, and the nation.

In 1914 the Smith-Lever Act was passed, and the Cooperative Extension Service was born. Historians call it the "starting mark" of club work, later to be known as "4-H" club work.[1] The idea of such an organization among rural youth had been generated in many places at least a decade before. But the year of 1914 is the one credited as the "official" beginning of club work. In this year governmental agencies, through specially trained personnel, began to work with rural boys and girls.

The first 50 years of Missouri club work are the subject matter of this book. The period it covers is between 1914 and 1964. During that half-century, one-half million of Missouri's young people were enrolled in this State's Extension youth program. In the very early years, the program operated under the general title of *Boys and Girls Club Work.* Came 1927, and its name was changed to *4-H Club Work.* In recent years the youth program has been broadened to encompass more than 4-H work, and to reach small town and city youth. It is a notable tribute to the elasticity of the program that it changes as times and conditions warrant.

Once a completely rural organization—rural including villages and small towns as well as open country—it is still deep-rooted in the farms of America and will always be, but its branches today reach into the cities and large towns of this America of ours, broadening the program and reaching thousands more.

---

[1] From a 4-H Club Leaflet, History of 4-H Club Work, (Columbia, Missouri, State 4-H Council, 1958-1959), P. 2.

The organization of this youth work involves the enrollment of members 9 to 19 years of age. By actual count of names on file in the 4-H Club State Office at the University of Missouri - Columbia, some 412,613 Missouri young people joined the 4-H clubs or became members during the years 1935-1964. Total enrollment during the years 1914-1935 was 211,688. So a half million is not an unrealistic figure.

Every historical detail embracing such a long period of such a complicated program cannot be included in one small volume. Some things of interest to many members and their parents, no doubt, have been of necessity omitted, or simply overlooked. But errors have not been intentional and have been mistakes of the hand rather than the heart.

In reading this history you will quickly understand that the key word is "work." That is true in the entire 4-H program. The members have been industrious, purposeful, and a joy to their supervisors and leaders.

To the half-million members to whom this book largely is "their story" should be added thousands of adults, serving in many capacities as voluntary 4-H leaders. They are "the carriers of water and the hewers of stone." How many adults fall into this classification no one will ever know. Their names are legion, and they served and still serve for that greater compensation—a feeling of having helped a boy or girl.

The guidance and the counseling given by these adults to the youth of Missouri through the 4-H program represents the very cornerstone of character building. It is the "warp and woof" of an educational fabric that grows stronger with the passage of time.

The family, or home, is the base of 4-H operations. Four-H work starts in the home with a boy and a girl, and so often it becomes "a family affair" with everyone from grandson and granddaughter to grandpa and grandma taking an interest. Here then is the true laboratory for character building. In 4-H club work we find *Character Building* at its best.

The program of 4-H has been termed "the program that turned kids on." It proved to be the inspirational dynamo for rural, and later for urban youth, at a strategic time in America's growth, shortly after the century's turn. No less now than then it continues to be a mighty inspirational and educational force in the lives of America's boys and girls. Through sympathetic leaders they find in it a beacon light to guide them in those important youthful years.

For those of us who have been especially commissioned to work closely with the Missouri boys and girls, related through this document, our years have been ones of challenging experiences. We feel humble to have been chosen. Often we have felt inadequate in meeting this tremendous responsibility.

It can be said of club youth as the naturalist has said of the leaves of the oak—*no two are alike.* Nor does the man or the woman who works with them remain the same after the rich, rewarding experience. "We never tire of the drama of the sunset," says Thoreau. Neither do we tire of youth!

This book is not the endeavor of one person. It is the work of many. It is the compounded inspiration of a half century brought together in an interesting narrative, fact-filled and conveniently placed between the covers of one volume.

Some have done more toward this book's research, writing, editing, and preparation of copy for the printers, than others. Those who have done much include T. T. Martin and Robert S. Clough, former State 4-H leaders, and Jane Hinote, who for many years was a member of the State 4-H staff. Clyde H. Duncan, our narrator, has taken a mountain of research material and woven it into a book. Mr. Duncan was himself a charter member of the organization about which he writes, and in 1955 received the National 4-H Alumni Award. He is a former member of the faculty of the College of Agriculture of the University of Missouri-Columbia, and author of several books including *STRAIGHT FURROWS. The Story of 4-H Club Work* and *FIND A CAREER IN AGRICULTURE.*

What then are the purposes of this book?

They are: To present the history of a successful voluntary informal educational youth program, and to emphasize the part played by young people, including their objectives, achievements, and individual growth through experience.

One of the purposes of this book is to stress group achievement and growth using the procedures and idealism of a democracy. Another purpose is to acquaint readers with a force, modest but dynamic, that is helping ambitious youth into paths that lead to good citizenship. There is in these pages the story of a program that embodies the four-fold development of the head, heart, hands, and health, of which the 4-H emblem is symbolic.

This narrative relating to a half-century of Missouri 4-H work was written to stimulate appreciation of the dignity of *WORK* and the value of *Creative Leisure Time Pursuits.* In these pages is shown a pattern for cooperative effort between professional and voluntary youth workers, all with the same objectives.

This book presents to the reader the contribution that has been made by voluntary leaders in all phases of 4-H training. It makes plain the part played by business and professional people in motivations of the highest caliber. Then, too, it is a written report of 50 years, a half-century of records, and as such should rest nobly on any library shelf awaiting to be read by the curious and the calculating, and should lie snugly in the archives for the use of future historians and researchers, its place well-earned.

But perhaps one of its chief aims will be to signal a new day in the University of Missouri Extension youth programs. It will serve to herald the beginning of another era, the second 50 years of the golden twentieth century. The strands of that fabric are already being fed into the loom.

No one doubts but what the next 50 years will be filled with as many, or more, achievements for the youth of Missouri, and for the adults who work with them, as were the first 50 . . . glorious, glamorous days about which this book, factual to its very end, but with a seemingly touch of the fictional in its power to interest.

Chapter I

IN THE BEGINNING

The Morrill Act . . . The Hatch Act . . .
Country-Life Commission . . .
Pre-Extension Work . . . The Smith-Lever Act

It was July 2, 1862,[2] at the very heighth of the Civil War, that President Lincoln signed the Land-Grant College Act.

As the century passed this day was to be known as the birth date of a national system of education for the poor as well as for the privileged. Time was to prove it the real beginning of 4-H club work. Had the Land-Grant Colleges never been brought into existence it is very doubtful if 4-H club work, as we know it today, would ever have been born.

The significance of this day in history, especially in 4-H history, should not be passed over lightly. It is well to reflect upon the details of that day as time and history recorded them.

Justin Morrill (the Vermont Senator entrusted by Lincoln to handle the legislative matters pertaining to the Civil War) and Jonathan Baldwin Turner (a Yale graduate and then a teacher at Illinois College at Jacksonville) had worked together tirelessly for the Land Grant College bill's passage. Turner has been termed "The Father of the Land Grant College."[3],[4] President Buchanan, before Lincoln, had vetoed a similar bill during his term of office.[5] Now one more friendly to the cause of education for the poor occupied the White House. Lincoln had known nothing but poverty throughout his youth and early manhood.

---

[2] Harry Edward Pratt, *Lincoln Day by Day,* 1840-1846 (Springfield, Ill.: The Abraham Lincoln Ass'n., 1939). Information about Lincoln and his activities on July 2, 1862, taken from volume in this series: Lincoln, from Jan. 1, 1840 to Dec. 31, 1842.

[3] Eloise P. Bingham, *The Stalwart Professor* (Mount Morris, Ill., Illinois State Teacher's Ass'n., Nov., 1935, Publishers, "The Illinois Teacher"), P. 81-82.

[4] Henry Steele Commager, *Documents of American History* (New York, Appleton-Century-Crofts, 1963), P. 412.

[5] Committee on Agriculture House of Representatives, 89th Congress, *Men and Milestones in American Agriculture,* (Washington D.C., U.S. Government Printing Office, 1966), P. 13.

On this day of July 2, 1862, the bill lay in its final drafted form. It lay in a mass of miscellany on the desk of the President, awaiting his signature. But there were delays before Abraham Lincoln placed his name to the document and made it one of the most conspicious laws of the century.

An orderly came in and announced that Congressman George W. Julian of Indiana wanted to discuss with the President the Civil War's outlook, and to consider what action would be taken to insure more Union victories. The President would have to defend General George B. McClellan from his critics. He wondered at the fate of the Army of the Potomac, now in its last days of fighting the Seven Days' Battle under this lackadaisical commander. Later that day he would learn of the attempt to take Richmond, thwarted largely because of McClellan's slowness and indecisiveness.

That hot July day was a busy one for Abraham Lincoln. There were problems involving looking after the welfare of Negroes fleeing from Southern bondage, conferences with Senators, innumerable letters to be written to people protesting the war effort. Then there was the signing of a treaty with the Ottoman Empire, which had to be done. Yet Lincoln, before the day's close, put his signature on what has become known as the Magna Carta of American education—the Land-Grant College Bill.

Some call it the Morrill Act in honor of its Congressional sponsor, Justin Smith Morrill. Essentially it provided for the establishment of colleges of agriculture and mechanic arts in all of the states. These colleges were to be financed by funds derived from the sale of vast acreages of lands then in the public domain.[6]

With the passage of the Land-Grant College Act, it became necessary for each state to enact enabling legislation to make this new law operative.

In Missouri, the provisions of the Morrill Act of 1862 were agreed to and accepted by the State's Twenty-Second General Assembly in a joint resolution passed March 17, 1863. Because of the Civil War, and of widespread and prolonged disagreement over the location of the Missouri College of Agriculture, the General Assembly did not agree on the establishment of the institution until 1870. But on February 24 a bill was passed and signed by Governor Joseph McClurg. This bill finally authorized the College of Agriculture and Mechanic Arts, as a division of the University of Missouri at Columbia.[7]

This marked the highlight of prolonged efforts, first recorded in 1852, to include agriculture in the courses of study offered by the University. It was part of a nation-wide movement to pull away from the established pattern of higher education, which stressed the classics, humanities and languages, and to develop practical programs which would more nearly meet the needs of a nation which still had much pioneering to do and which had vast acreage yet undeveloped and cities yet unborn.

With the establishment of colleges of agriculture, it was not long before educators realized that no great body of knowledge existed in regard to farming as a science such as existed in other fields such as medicine, law, and theology. Teachers

---

[6]Committee on Agriculture, House of Representatives, 89th Congress, *Men and Milestones in American Agriculture,* (Washington, D.C., U.S. Government Printing Office, 1966), P. 13.

[7]John H. Longwell, from the unpublished manuscript of the former Dean of the Missouri College of Agriculture, Titled: *The Missouri College of Agriculture, 1938-1970.*

attempting to instruct classes in various areas of agriculture "soon ran out of ammunition." As a result, class attendance dropped very fast and a major problem confronted the whole idea of agricultural colleges as educational institutions.

The experience of the Missouri College of Agriculture was similar to that of all other Land-Grant Colleges which had been established under the new law. The extreme lack of technical agricultural information could be remedied only by research programs which could determine how the basic principles of science could be applied to farm production.

To solve this problem there was to come in 1887 what is known as the Hatch Act, sponsored by a Missourian, Congressman William H. Hatch of Hannibal.[8] It authorized the establishment of an experiment station as a department of each college of agriculture. Money would be appropriated by the Federal and State governments to help pay the costs of establishing and operating the station.[9]

The Missouri Agricultural Experiment Station was established in January, 1888, under the terms of the Hatch Act. Thus began in this state scientific research aimed at building a fund of agricultural knowledge. This was needed if agriculture as a science was to be taught in classrooms and laboratories as theories, and if new and improved techniques were to be put into practice in fields and feedlots of Missouri farmers. All this had to precede the youth program (which would be known as club work) for without it the tools of education were few, and 4-H club work is education.

It was a natural process that grew out of the Land-Grant Colleges and the State Experiment Stations that brought forth the enactment of the Smith-Lever Bill on May 8, 1914. This Bill provided for the Cooperative Extension Service. It was best identified in the public mind in that early day by the work of the county and home demonstration agents.

As the Experiment Station, through the Hatch Act, became the strong left arm of the colleges of agriculture, providing scientific knowledge related to agriculture, so did the Cooperative Extension Service become the strong right arm, making for the full and healthful creation of an entirely new education organism. It is recognized throughout the world as one of the most outstanding innovations in education, unique to America. Its purpose has aimed at developing, through education, inspiration, and competition over the long run, better and happier citizens.

The enactment of the Smith-Lever Act in 1914 came after a half-dozen years of hard effort on the part of the Land-Grant Colleges, and a corresponding effort by its friends among the agricultural leaders of the nation.[10,11] As early as 1908, the colleges were talking among themselves about a plan for Federal aid involving an outright grant to each state of $10,000, in addition to a similar amount based on

[8]Gladys L. Baker, Wayne E. Rasmussen, Vivian Wiser and Jane M. Porter: *Century of Service, The First 100 Years of the U.S.D.A.*, (Washington, D.C., U.S. Government Printing Office, 1963), P. 24-25.

[9]Henry Steele Commager, *Documents of American History*, (New York, Appleton-Century-Crofts, 1963), P. 575.

[10]Franklin M. Reck, *The 4-H Story*, (Ames, Iowa, Iowa State University Press, 1951), P. 118-132.

[11]Sol Holt, *The Dictionary of American History*, (New York, N.Y., MacFadden-Bartell Corporation, 1964), P. 327.

rural population. These amounts were to be provided each state if it matched these funds.

The air literally was full of ideas pertaining to agriculture in those days. There was a national awareness that farming and those affiliated with it, were coming into their own. National and state governments, business, and industry were all cooperating in new programs aimed at helping agriculture.

Up in Iowa, Perry G. Holden, the tall, bearded agronomist of Iowa State College, was conducting the first agricultural trains across that state, and crusading for improved seed corn with what he called "the rag-doll seed corn testing method."[12] He backed improved agricultural practices with the zeal of an evangelist as he trumpeted across the corn belt with a message of "Test, Don't Guess."[13]

The President of the United States, Theodore Roosevelt, alert to all that was going on about him, caught the spirit of the times and called for a National Rural Life Conference at the White House, May 13-15, 1908. He appointed on August 10, 1908, Liberty Hyde Bailey, the "Grand Old Man of Horticulture," then teaching at Cornell University, to head the *Country Life Commission.*[14] Bailey believed, as so many did then, that the greatest problems facing American agriculture were more economic and social than technical.

Serving with Bailey on the Country Life Commission in 1908 was a notable group of the nation's educational leaders. Their's was an intensive study of the government of rural communities as well as of the religious, recreational, health, and educational problems. State-wide meetings were held throughout the country, and the suggestions of rural leaders were discussed, and acted upon.

The Country Life Commission sought long range objectives for bettering the lot of farm people and their children. Its findings became a sort of prophecy, and they tended to focus a national spotlight on the farmer's social rights, which have carried down to the present day.

In rural education, the Commission found that the country school did not relate itself closely enough to the environment of the boy and girl. There was a real need for a more practical educational approach to farming. The Commission stressed the need in its report for increased college services through an enlarged Extension Service of specialists. These specialists would reach the multitudes, right down to the "one-gallused farmer" and his mule and "bull-tongue" plow.

So it came about that in 1909 the Congressional hopper was filled with several bills providing for Extension work and for the teaching of vocational agriculture in the schools. The first of many bills introduced was one by Congressman J. C. McLaughlin of Michigan. He had endorsed and worked for corn clubs in his state. The McLaughlin Bill provided $10,000 per state, plus added funds to be matched by the various states, following the suggestions by the Land-Grant Colleges. The Bill was introduced on December 15, 1909.

---

[12] Perry G. Holden, *"Test Don't Guess",* (Chicago, Ill., Privately printed by The International Harvester Co., 1916), P. 1-30.
[13] Franklin M. Reck, *The 4-H Story,* (Ames, Iowa: Iowa State University Press, 1951), P. 37-39.
[14] From U.S.D.A. Yearbook, *A Century of Service,* (Washington, D.C., U.S. Government Printing Office, 1963), P. 521.

It was this kind of bill which eventually became law some five years later and became known as the Smith-Lever Act.[15] This Act provided for the national establishment of what is now generally known as the Cooperative Extension Service. It took five years to thresh out the many existing ideas of just what was wanted in this area. Congress wasn't certain just how it wanted to go about aiding agriculture. But with the passage of the Smith-Lever Act, May 8, 1914, the way was cleared for the beginning of a new day in American agriculture.

The fathers of this important Act were Congressman A. F. Lever of South Carolina and Senator Hoke Smith of Georgia.[16] Lever had been elected to Congress first in 1901. In 1902 he began to notice the excellent work being done in his own state by what were known as "Farmers' Cooperative Demonstration Workers."

Congressman Lever observed the rapid growth of the new movement known as "Club Work" among rural youth, especially in growing corn. He had become an ardent follower of the educational ideas being put forth then by Dr. Seaman A. Knapp, known as "a demonstration plot evangelist."[17] These proved in time to be the basic ideas which would be adopted and used by the Extension Service.

Senator Smith, like Congressman Lever, was a "demonstration work" enthusiast. He had been an Altanta lawyer and later Governor of Georgia, during which time he had been instrumental in providing wagons and workshop equipment for the first consolidated school in Georgia.

Senator Smith had been an enthusiastic supporter of club work in his state, and he had endorsed funds to be used by Georgia's College of Agriculture for its own special brand of Extension work. So it was natural after his election to the United States Senate in 1911 that he worked for passage of the Lever Bill in the Senate. The Lever Bill was the successor to the McLaughlin Bill in the House of Representatives.

By 1913 all obstacles to the Bill had been cleared away in the National Congress, and in May of the following year the Smith-Lever Bill, as it is commonly named out of respect to its two sponsors, was passed. On the day of the passage of the Act, May 8, 1914, the Extension Service, as we know it today, was born.

With the coming of the newly created Cooperative Extension Service, in cooperation with states and counties, and with the placing immediately of county and home demonstration agents in many of the counties of the nation, club work gained a new ally. Rural boys and girls, many of whom had been active in corn, pig and canning clubs under a galaxy of sponsors (largely school teachers and public-spirited business people who worked on a voluntary basis), had exchanged these amateur helpers for highly qualified Extension workers known generally as county and home demonstration agents. By now the boys and girls had a real "friend in court."

It was natural that those who became engaged in the new program of Cooperative Extension work brought about by the enactment of the Smith-Lever Bill, would find attentive ears, and eager hands, among the thousands of farm boys and girls of the nation.

---

[15]Ibid, p. 118-132.
[16]Franklin M. Reck, The 4-H Story, (Ames, Iowa, Iowa State University Press, 1951), p. 119-120.
[17]Ibid, P. 50, 295.

Soon after the enactment of the Bill, and almost as soon as county and home agents had gotten settled in their counties, they began to take over the work of organizing various clubs throughout their areas. They gradually assumed tasks started by county school superintendents, working with school room teachers.

They had done a good job, all of them, with their club programs. They had carried on in their limited way with a new educational idea, and with few tools to work with, and they had encouraged youth in a program which overnight seemed to become nationally acceptable, and popular with adults as well as youth.

But with the coming of the county and home agents a new day dawned for America's rural youth. The county agents, at the very beginning of their work, carried on the club program, much as did the county school superintendents, relying heavily upon the school room. But since the schools were in session only a portion of the year, this plan left the summer months—the months when demonstration plots could be growing—with no program to occupy the boy and girl.

In the beginning, club work in Missouri was built on one basic simple idea . . . that the member would elect to assume a responsibility and carry it out at home in line with his own needs. The member would raise a calf, preserve the family food supply, beautify a room or home surroundings. In doing so the member would use approved practices and methods. *The objective was to provide a practical education for boys and girls and to induce them to use more productive methods.*

The rural part of the United States lagged behind towns and cities. A rural youth program based on the approved methods of farming which would increase the economic base of the rural areas was badly needed. A practical type of education was sought which would induce youth to use better methods of farming practices as they evolved.

Four-H club work was born out of the situation of the times right after the turn of the 20th century. *Thus, we found the purpose and emphasis in 4-H rested on the project and what the boy or girl could produce.*

Early in the 20th century there was a definite educational gap between the development of proper methods and new information, and their adoption by farmers. One purpose of boy and girl club work, as it was labeled at that time, was to reach the father through the son with new information in agriculture.

In a short time boys and girls who enrolled in various club projects, under the leadership of county extension agents, found there was work to be done by the hands in planning and growing an acre of corn or cotton, depending upon the area. Others found their work in growing a pig or a calf, or, in the case of the girl members, in growing 1/16th acre of tomatoes, and canning the crop by the then famous "cold-pack" method.

Thus work and pleasure combined to keep them busy in a full year's program. Records had to be kept, and so there came into being for the nation's enthusiastic club members a well-planned and organized system, calculated toward making the individual youth a better citizen.

The Extension agents took the latest knowledge in many areas of crop and livestock production, as determined by their colleges through their experiment stations, out to the farmers and their families. Many county Extension agents in those days, unable to reach adults directly were able to do so indirectly through their children who were enrolled in club work. Club work thus early became a valuable vehicle through which the teaching of the Land-Grant College should be conveyed to the nation's farmers.

D. Howard Doane, founder of the Doane Agricultural Service, St. Louis, Mo., and former head of the farm management staff of the Missouri College of Agriculture, is credited with starting county agent work in Missouri even before passage of the Smith-Lever Act in 1914. Under Mr. Doane's leadership some 13 county agents were appointed.

In June of 1914, A. J. Meyer was made Director of Extension work. R. H. Emberson was put in charge of Boys and Girls Club work before the passage of the Smith-Lever Act. His work was started in Missouri March 1, 1914, two months before the Act's passage. His official appointment as an Extension worker became effective June 8, 1914.

During that first year, club work was confined to corn projects for boys, and tomato projects for girls. In 1915, Mr. Emberson was quoted as saying, "Whenever possible, clubs are organized in connection with rural schools; and the teacher acts as local leader."

In that same year, 1915, Mr. Meyer reported, "Six of the Farm Advisors and five University Board of Curator members believe that most emphasis should be placed upon boys and girls work."

So in the very beginning the Extension Service claimed club work as its own. It expected the program to function largely through the schools as it had done during the years before Extension existed.

Early Extension workers appointed by D. Howard Doane included the following 13 people:

County	Agent	Date Appointed		
Cape Girardeau	C. M. McWilliams	Aug.	1,	1912
Pettis	S. M. Jordan	Jan.	1,	1913
	(Sam Jordan actually started at an earlier date sponsored by a group of local Pettis County businessmen.)			
Buchanan	*F. W. Faurot	Mar.	1,	1913
Johnson	C. M. Long	Mar.	1,	1913
Audrain	*E. W. Rusk	Apr.	1,	1913
Dade	E.J. Rodekohr	Apr.	1,	1913
Jackson	E. A. Ikenberry	Apr.	20,	1913
Marion	H. H. Lade	Apr.	21,	1913
Scott	H. B. Derr	Sept.	15,	1913
Cooper	J. D. Wilson	Sept.	24,	1913
Greene	E. A. Cockefair	Feb.	1,	1914
St. Francois	James Derr	Feb.	2,	1914
Saline	Paul Maris	June	15,	1914

* Of interest to many Missourians: F. W. Faurot is the father of Don Faurot, former football coach and later athletic director at the University of Missouri. Mr.

Delegates from Johnson County to the 1914 University of Missouri Farmer's Week.

Judging mules at the 1914 Junior Farm and Home Week.

Four-H club tour in Lafayette County, 1920. F. W. Caldwell, county agent.

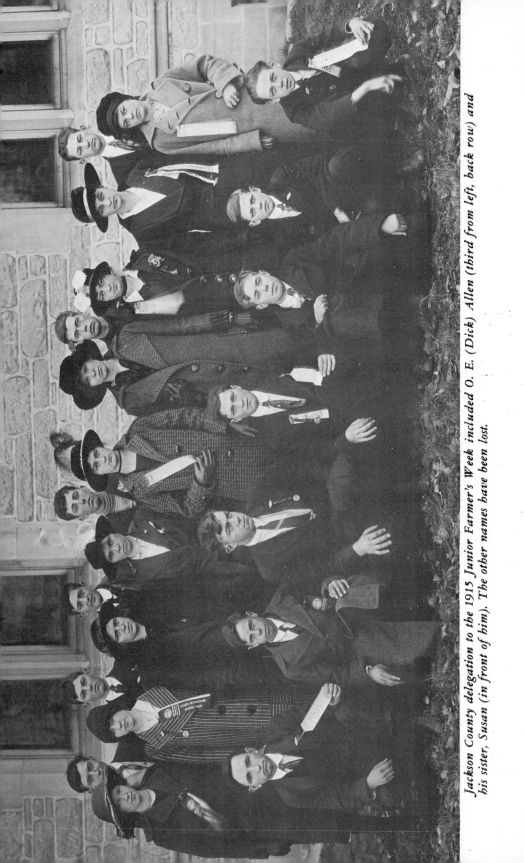

Jackson County delegation to the 1915 Junior Farmer's Week included O. E. (Dick) Allen (third from left, back row) and his sister, Susan (in front of him). The other names have been lost.

Faurot is 94 years of age as this manuscript is written. E. W. Rusk is a brother of the late H. P. Rusk who was Dean of the Illinois College of Agriculture for many years. R. J. Howat and his father, John Howat, were both county agents at the same time in "The Twenties." R. J. was agent for Jackson County and John was agent for Randolph County.

Other early staff members included:

County	Agent	Date	
Carroll	W. M. Cook	Jan.	1, 1915
Butler	T. M. Tolson	Jan.	25, 1915
St. Francois	B. L. France	Feb.	16, 1915
Buchanan	L. V. Caldwell	Apr.	4, 1915
Knox	F. E. Longmire	May	20, 1915
St. Charles	W. R. Hendrix	Aug.	1, 1915
Saline	R. J. Howat	Dec.	17, 1915
Carroll	R. D. Jay	June	16, 1916

Girls club work started without help from county home economics Extension workers. Babb Bell and Nelle Nesbit started as state workers with girls in 1917. As World War I began a number of emergency district workers were added. However, two county home demonstrators were employed in 1917. They were Bertha Adams in Dunklin County on December 7, 1917, and Irene F. Blood in Atchison County on December 10, 1917. Other very early home demonstration workers with dates of first employment include:

Name	County	Date	
Mary Moreland	Johnson	Mar.	18, 1918
Florence Carvin	Jackson	Mar.	26, 1918
Katherine Brand	Dunklin	June	1, 1918
Jane Hinote	Cape Girardeau	July	1, 1918
Helen Glasse	Chariton	Aug.	1, 1918
Lula Morris	Livingston	Aug.	1, 1918
Alene Hinn	Cole	Aug.	16, 1918
Signe Freestrom	Lincoln	Sept.	1, 1918
Margaret Nelson	Linn	Sept.	1, 1918
Mildred Glasse	Lafayette	Sept.	16, 1918
Iola George	Harrison	Oct.	1, 1918

One of the most interesting counties in Missouri, with a vigorous county school superintendent, is credited with starting in 1914 the first corn clubs in Missouri. The man was B. P. Burnham and the first Corn Club he started was in an Ironton school on Knob Street in Iron County.

Chapter II

MISSOURI'S FIRST CLUBS

Iron County and B.P. Burnham

It seems providential that the area where the first club work would begin in Missouri would be Iron County, some 86 miles south of St. Louis. Here is a beautiful, rugged country steeped in historical lore that dates back to *ante-bellum* days.

Here it was that Fort Davison, utilizing the natural terrain and protection of old Pilot Knob, for a short time stayed the onrushing Confederate Army, and thus effected a delay long enough to provide the protection for St. Louis, which was one of the centers of gunsmithing for the Union Army.

This was in the County of Iron, noted for its vast natural beauty, epitomized best perhaps by the scenic Arcadia Valley which has been for years the rendezvous of religious groups in summer camps.

Here, beside a small spring on the property of James Lindsay in what is now the heart of Ironton, the county seat, Ulysses S. Grant received in 1861 from President Lincoln the commission of Brigadier General.[18] Thus the Civil War leader received his first military star from that very spot in Iron County and began his long climb up the ladder that was to lead finally to the White House. Today Iron County is part of the historical legend not only of Missouri, but of America as well.

Iron County was established by a special act of the State Legislature on February 17, 1857. There is a natural toughness about this country best symbolized by the great outcroppings of granite and by the sort of men and women it has produced through its long history.

Outstanding among these men was B. P. Burnham, who as Iron County's superintendent of schools, is credited with organizing in 1914 the first corn clubs in Missouri. These corn clubs, as so many did in those days, came into being through the facilities of the school room, and through the help of sympathetic teachers.

---

[18] From the records of the *Missouri Historical Society,* Columbia, Mo. (A memorial plaque commemorating the event was erected on the spot in Ironton by the Missouri Historical Society).

It was natural that Mr. Burnham, perhaps after receiving information on how to organize clubs from R. H. Emberson, State Club Leader from 1914 to 1923, went first to the high school on Knob Street in Ironton. At that time it had been a high school for only two years. Here the county school superintendent found teachers who were willing to help with the first club organization, and here he found seven members who agreed to each grow an acre of corn.

Encouraged by his first attempt to start a corn club in the Ironton school, Superintendent Burnham next turned his attention to the little village of Annapolis, eighteen miles south of Ironton, and it was here he "stirred up interest" in club work in what was then known as the King School, east a short distance of the little town. Melvin J. Kelly was named to serve as the second corn club's leader.

One of the nine members of the Annapolis Club, and one who still resides in that area is Frank Morris. He says with genuine pleasantness, "I can still see Mr. Burnham, a big man with lots of foresight. I still have my old corn club record book. I look at it every now and then and recall those pleasant days. We had six or eight members in our club, and our teacher then was Mr. John L. Hickman. We were required to grow one acre of corn, and we measured the yields. We applied bone meal and barnyard manure to the soil before planting the corn. That was the general recommendation for all Missouri corn club members back then."

Mr. Morris recalls that as Mr. Burnham went to the various county schools, usually on horseback, he recognized a need for club work as it was known then. "The county school superintendent was the only person we had to help us organize any kind of club, or to help create interest in anything dealing with agriculture," Mr. Morris says. "Mr. Burnham was a real pioneer in good agricultural practices. His interests in corn club work and in promoting the use of improved seed were very sincere".

It is well to dwell for a little while on this man Burnham and on the times that produced him, since he contributed so much to the first club organized in the state. He was a large man, six-feet, two inches tall; and he weighed more than 200 pounds. He was a gentle person, with an academic bearing, with blue eyes and dark hair; but when occasion demanded it he could be as hard as the flint of his own Iron County.

The story is related by his son, Edwin, now a resident of Overland, Missouri, that when his father was Iron County Treasurer a St. Louis man who owned property in that county came into his office to pay taxes. On finding the taxes larger than he thought they should be, he refused to make the payment. The St. Louis man had laid his overcoat on a chair nearby while he talked with Burnham, the treasurer. Mr. Burnham noting the expensive overcoat picked it up, and as he did he addressed the owner sternly, "No taxes, no overcoat."

In those days any personal property could be attached for tax payments by the tax collector. "Realizing this, the man quickly paid his taxes," Edwin Burnham says, "and dad returned him the coat. It well illustrates how my father could react under unfavorable circumstances."

The senior Burnham, the man who first organized two corn clubs in Iron County, was a community leader. He was a member of the Masonic and Odd Fellows Lodges and the Modern Woodmen of America Fraternal Order.

During much of his long lifetime from April 9, 1875, to March 6, 1964, a period of 89 years, he served as a member of the Ironton school board, and for a while was its secretary. His church membership was with the Methodists where he was a member of the official board. He also was a choir member and Sunday School teacher. He served one year as treasurer of "Epworth Among the Hills," at nearby Arcadia, a Methodist retreat. Here assembled each year hundreds of Methodists for church and youth leadership conferences.[19]

Mr. Burnham's was a well-rounded life as teacher, county school commissioner, and later as county superintendent of schools. He was a "natural" teacher, and taught a rural school at the age of 70. He served Iron County also as treasurer as well as tax collector. For a time he was cashier of the Iron County Security Bank in the county seat. In his later years he served as an appraiser for the Veterans Administration and made reports for Dun and Bradstreet.

He was educated at Marvin College (then a Methodist Institution at Fredericktown, Missouri, later merged with Central College at Fayette). He also attended Southeast Missouri State College at Cape Girardeau. Feeling that some day he would need to know more about the modern techniques of business, he enrolled in and graduated from the Gem City Business College at Quincy, Illinois.

In 1961, three years before his death, he was honored for his interest in 4-H club work during the Iron County Fair and Horseshow at Ironton. He was presented a 4-H Meritorious Service Plaque by Mrs. A. M. Barber, then the president of the Iron County 4-H Council. Frank Adams, representing the University of Missouri Extension Council, presided at the ceremonies honoring the man who had started the first two clubs in the state.

The clubs were organized at Ironton and Annapolis sometime before the end of the 1913-1914 school terms. This gave each corn club member time to spend the summer months growing the acre of corn as part of his corn club project.

The year of 1914 was an interesting year for club work's birth. Had Mr. Burnham listened attentively on that day when he made his way to the Ironton School on Knob Street to organize the first club, he might have heard strains of "The Missouri Waltz" coming from the Academy of Music, Ironton's cultural center, located on the right hand side of Main Street in the second block north of the court house.

That was the year the Missouri Waltz was written. That was the year when an Ironton resident as he walked around "the square" would have observed a motley assortment of business houses, including the Commercial, Kessling and American Hotels, rendezvous of traveling men. He would have seen Hanson's Blacksmith Shop, where farmers could get a horse shod for a dollar and Nickels Meat Market, where a pound of the best steak could be bought for twenty cents. There was Kanouse's Valley Inn, and Mayes and Weaver Feed and Sale Stable, where traveling salesmen rented a two-horse rig for two dollars and a half a day.[20]

On "the square" was a flour mill, Whitworth's Hardware Store and the Iron County Bank. There was Jake Grandhomme's Candy Kitchen, hangout of the Tom Sawyers and the place where the young blades bought taffy for their sweethearts.

---

[19]From the 1964 files of *The Ironton Register,* Ironton, Missouri.
[20]From the files of the *Ironton Register,* Ironton Missouri, and *Arcadia Valley Enterprise,* Arcadia, Missouri.

There was Conway's Barber Shop, where the latest yarn was spun and sideburns clipped, and there was Adolph's Jewelry Store, where wide-band, gold wedding rings could be bought at special $1.50 rates.

Gay's Blacksmith Shop, John Left's Restaurant and Rooming House, Baldwin Brothers' Store, Schultze's Pool Hall, where men idled away many a pleasant hour, Dr. Kenneth Huston's Office, the Bank of Ironton, Gay and Kendall General Store, Fletchers and Bargers Store were all part of the local scene.

Then too there was Dr. Marshall's office, the Post Office, Iron County Register Newspaper Office, Percy's Hardware Store, Woodside's Style Shop, Rosentreader's Livery Stable, the Blue Store and Ice Cream Parlor, and Reicks Undertaker Parlor.

They were all there, on or near the square, and further on up the street was the Lopez Store, known far and wide throughout the valley as a leader in country merchandizing.

Nationally, 1914 was a year to be remembered. It was the year in which World War I began, a world-shaking event that reshaped the histories of all the nations of the earth. But as yet the American people were relatively unconcerned with happenings in Europe.

In America ragtime was the rage, bringing with it such lively and picturesquely named dances as the "turkey trot," the "grizzly bear" and the "Texas Tommy." Glamorous Irene and Vernon Castle helped to popularize these new dances. Cubism was the new shocker in the art world. Fashionable New Yorkers were discovering ping-pong.

Movies, which had been shown in cramped, smelly nickelodeons up to now were acquiring theaters of their own. Keith's Vaudeville was stirring the entertainment world, and Charlie Chaplin began making two-reel comedies. Theda Bara was immortalizing the Vamp with her black-ringed eyes. Mack Sennett introduced his bathing beauties, and the first wave of great movie stars was arriving, Mary Pickford, Douglas Fairbanks, Charlie Chaplin, William S. Hart, and Wallace Reid.

The Stutz automobile people that year brought out their "Bearcat," and added to the epic of that day the linen-duster clad chauffeur, with handle-bar moustache, and ever-smoking fat cigar. Henry Ford's "Tin Lizzie," on the scene now only a decade, was stirring up the dust of country lanes as people talked about good roads, the new fangled filling-stations and high taxes.

Ty Cobb's name was on the lips of every baseball lover as Cobb streaked the bases and man-handled the umpires. Billy Sunday chose that year of 1914 to give up his baseball career with the Chicago White Sox and to hit the sawdust trail of evangelism.

Those were the days when small boys and girls in pig-tails were humming "Alexander's Ragtime Band," "Waiting for the Robert E. Lee," "It's a Long, Long Way to Tipperary," and "I'm Forever Blowing Bubbles."

The summer Chautauquas were in full bloom with long nightly programs in the tank towns across America, and the local subscribers would have their pick of two big attractions—William Jennings Bryan, with variations of his "Cross of Gold" speech, or an off-Broadway cast of professional actors in a melodrama, "The

Drunkard," that was wetting many eyes. It was a great time to be alive, but many lives were soon to be lost in World War I.[21]

Here in the United States people were more concerned in early 1914 with events at home than with a war brewing in Europe. When men from the USS Dolphin were arrested by Mexican authorities in Tampico in April, 1914, and when Marines occupied the City of Vera Cruz, the nation began to get excited.

But the news of the assassination of Archduke Franz Ferdinand in Serbia on June 28 had to compete for newspaper headlines with the Suffragettes' march on the nation's Capitol. Few in America believed that the happenings in Serbia would provide the spark for a major war. But a month later, Austria declared war on that country, and before long the dogs of war were on the loose and much of Europe soon became involved. On August 4, President Woodrow Wilson proclaimed the neutrality of the United States, a status that proved difficult to maintain, and on April 6, 1917 Congress declared war with Germany.[22]

August, 1914, was also an important month for American shipping. On the 15th of that month the Panama Canal was opened, shortening the water route between the Atlantic and the Pacific Oceans.

This was an era of change. Over seventy-three percent of the children were attending public day-schools. More students than ever before in the nation's history were graduating from high school. However, even in 1920, only about 17 percent achieved this goal. And this in a country where 33 percent of the people lived on farms, usually great distances from colleges and universities. Farm boys and girls in a situation such as this stood to gain from increased educational planning such as now was getting under way through the newly enacted Smith-Lever Act.

Farming then was quite different from now. Horses and mules provided most of the farm power. The country had 21,308,000 horses and 4,870,000 mules. Hay production was important at a time when even the Secretary of Agriculture, David Houston, who had been chancellor of Washington University in St. Louis, and before that President of Texas A and M College, depended upon a horse-drawn carriage for transporation in the City of Washington.

Approximately 82 million tons of hay were cut that year of 1914, with a low marketable value of $10.60 a ton.

In the year of 1914, the United States Department of Agriculture organized and expanded its Extension Work in cooperation with state and local agencies under authority of the Smith-Lever Act. Such Extension work soon increased to involve not only the adults on the farms, but the boys and girls as well.

All over America the seed of what would in time become known as 4-H club work had been planted. It followed the pattern of the work done in Iron County, Missouri, by B. P. Burnham. He planted the first seed in a fertile soil and promised an early inspiration for all who then, or later on, might participate. For his foresight and thoughtfulness his name is written large on Missouri's 4-H club golden scroll.

*   *   *

---

[21]Sol Holt, *The Dictionary of American History,* (New York, N.Y., MacFadden-Bartell Corporation, 1964), P. 376.
[22]Henry Steele Commager, Documents of American History (New York, N.Y., Appleton-Century-Crofts, 1963), P. 128.

Let's have a look at the successful techniques employed by leaders in helping members acquire the fundamentals of knowledge, develop the ability to think, and stimulate the urge to inquire.

Chapter III

THE CLUB

The Early Clubs . . . Camps and Roundups . . .
Boys and Girls Clubs . . . 4-H Clubs . . .
Clubs with Long Histories . . . The First 4-H Girls' Clubs

As noted before, the turn into the 20th century marked increasing interest in agriculture and youth work. This we have seen in corn growing contests for boys, some efforts in promoting boys camps, and some teaching of agriculture in rural schools before 1914.

The early development of organized group work with Missouri youth was largely stimulated by local conditions, by imaginative leadership within the state, and by successful pioneer work which was going on in various parts of America. There were four periods of club work development as indicated by available records.

The first period began in 1900 and was concluded by the passage of the Smith-Lever Act in 1914. This first period had its roots deep in the American public school system, and the teachers were the leaders. Usually they were all alone, but sometimes they had local assistance. This first period, from 1900 to 1914, is commonly referred to as "The pre-Extension period."

The second period, 1914-1920, was the time when voluntary leaders began to take over, and the third period embraces the time between the late 1920's to 1938 when "project clubs" with volunteer leaders came into existence.

The fourth period covers the years from 1938 to the present time, made noteworthy by emphasis on community club activities, with two kinds of volunteer leaders—the project leader and the community leader.

An example of these early days in the program was a flower garden contest among the boys and girls of the public schools of Columbia, Missouri. This was in 1900, under the guidance of R. H. Emberson.

The technical information was authored by Dr. J. C. Whitten, professor of horticulture at the University of Missouri at that time. Judging and the awarding of prizes were done by Mrs. C. B. Rollins, Mrs. Frances E. Poor, and Dr. Whitten.

From 1909 to 1914, attention was given to stimulating the interest of Missouri rural boys and girls in agriculture. This work was carried on through the Missouri schools while Mr. Emberson was State School Supervisor.

The first year included a study of the crops grown in the local communities. Practical problems were presented in testing, weighing, and judging different classes of grain. The second year's work dealt with types and breeds of livestock. Mr. Emberson became the first State Club Leader of Missouri in 1914.

Early Camps

In 1907, Samuel M. Jordan, a representative of the Missouri State Board of Agriculture, did some special work with Missouri farm boys. He conducted a series of encampments in which approved practices in agriculture were taught.

Three farm boys' encampments were held during the year. The first was conducted at the Glenview Farm near McCurdy in Mr. Jordan's home county of Gentry. It was held at his own expense, with 152 boys enrolled. Another camp was held in Bates County (sponsored by a banker and a farmer) with an enrollment of 180 boys. The largest encampment of 1907 was in Saline County, attended by 300 boys. It was sponsored by the Sweet Springs community. Other camps were held in following years.

Farm boys, 10 to 20 years of age, were invited to attend the camps for three days of study; and all, including adults, were invited to attend on the fourth and final day, known as "Everybody's Day."

The program was given by representatives of the Missouri State Board of Agriculture, by faculty members of the Missouri College of Agriculture, and by specialists of the U. S. Department of Agriculture. It included instruction periods, accompanied by experiments, practical farm demonstrations, supervised recreation, group discussion, and farm reports.

Corn clubs were organized at the close of each camp. They were not organized locally, because there was no Cooperative Extension Service to follow up these early endeavors, but the ideas and experiences survived and carried over until 1914. Then the U. S. Department of Agriculture and the state Land-Grant Colleges were made responsible for the conduct of Boys and Girls Club Work.

Interest in club work had now passed through that very early period known generally as "the days before the county agent."

To repeat for emphasis, what we know today as 4-H project work started officially with Cooperative Extension work in 1914.

The Smith-Lever Law was the third of a series of acts that provided for the Land-Grant College. First came the Morrill Act of 1862 that provided for the teaching of agriculture. This was followed by the Hatch Act of 1887 which provided for experiment stations to carry on research work. Then came Extension work which provided for the dissemination of knowledge in the fields of agriculture and homemaking and provided for county agents, or farm advisors as some were called in the beginning. Home demonstration agents, or home agents, followed very shortly after the introduction of the county agent.

Club work among the country's rural youth gained quick acceptance after the county agent began his work. Missouri's first two years' records in this interesting field showed outstanding achievement, as these tables show:

Project	1914 Clubs	Members	1915 Clubs	Members
Corn	40	423	41	1,178
Tomatoes	14	183		
Sewing	29	316	604	3,301
Canning	18	198	26	308
Bread Making	11	80	11	90
Poultry	29	317	72	937
Stock Judging	12	135	114	1,162
Totals	153	1,454	604	7,092

Not all who enrolled actually started work. One hundred fifty-nine completed the work in sewing, one in breadmaking, 22 in poultry, and 135 in livestock judging the first year!

Original enrollments by counties:

County	Agent	1914 Clubs	Members	1915 Clubs	Members
Audrain	Rusk	(Too scattered to organize)			
Buchanan	Faurot	5	103	26	465
Cape Girardeau	McWilliams	0		0	0
Cooper	Wilson	0		3	19
Dade	Rodekohr	5	30	0	
Greene	Cockefair	0		1	54
Jackson	Ikenberry	2	80	12	363
Johnson	Long	10	95	2	50
Marion	Gillman	0		0	
Pettis	Jordan	35	402	17	60
Saline	Maris	1	6	0	0
Scott	Derr	4	18	1	10
Butler	Tolson			11	93
Carroll	Cook				16

In 1916, 376 clubs had 3,715 members.

Change in Leadership at the Local Level

After World War I, the transition began from teacher-led clubs to clubs with voluntary leaders. Actually all leaders were voluntary, but it is necessary to understand that a difference existed.

Teacher-leaders took the initiative in organizing clubs. Many county school superintendents urged teachers to implement this movement as B. P. Burnham, the county school superintendent, had done in Iron County. Teacher-led clubs were usually restricted to the school year. This largely prevented club work during the growing and canning season and tended to discourage enrollment in projects that could not be completed during the school year. A great amount of excellent work was done under teacher leadership. The last day of school often featured the club work and created favorable comment from residents of the community.

Parents or other adult local residents are usually thought of as voluntary leaders. Canning clubs were usually led by voluntary leaders from the very beginning. Home economics club work "grew up" with girls' project work and provided a source for trained leaders.

Getting men to accept the responsibility of leadership often proved to be a hard task. Teaching, training, and organizing of subject matter were responsibilities that required more than average recruiting ability to get qualified and interested people to carry on the work.

Another way of designating the period which included the 1920's and well into the 1930's, is to refer to the period as the era of the "single project" club. That held true for both the voluntary and teacher-led clubs. Most clubs had a single leader. The period of activity started with the beginning of the project and on its completion it was truly ended. There was little carryover from one club year to the next. There were very few continuous clubs.

The annual reports of this period claimed that about 95 percent of the local leaders were teachers. However, the county extension agents and county home demonstration agents were guiding local leaders outside the school organization, in methods and subject matter. These experiences became the basis for the development of club work in the so-called third period of its organization.

Finally, on October 12, 1921, Director A. J. Meyer, acting for the College of Agriculture, directed that the organization of school clubs should be curtailed and more clubs should be organized under the Extension Service principles. The annual report of 1922 to the Federal Extension Service in Washington, D. C., did not include work done in those counties without Extension agents.

Stages of 4-H Club Development

The third period of club organization continued until 1938, when the project unit of organization was largely replaced by the community club plan.

The changes in Extension Service policy provided mainly for the following procedures:

a. The reorganized plan for conducting club work in Missouri became effective on December 1, 1921.

b. On that date, R. H. Emberson became a club specialist, with his activities limited to certain non-agent counties, working under a new project leader, who was designated later.

In 1923 T. T. Martin was appointed state leader of 4-H club work and Jane Hinote was appointed as state club agent, working with Mr. Martin as project leader. During the following years as club organization grew, a number of state club agents were added to the state staff.

As club work followed more closely the Extension Service principles of organization, the procedures likewise changed.

The Extension Service followed the educational principle known as "group work." The program was the peoples' program: Members worked largely upon their own problems and under their own leadership but with the guidance of the Extension Service.

Boys and girls club work followed the group work pattern: That is, in using democratic procedures, in working on problems through self-help programs, under the guidance of the Extension Service.

World War I Period

"World War I followed very quickly after the conception of the club program. During the war, emphasis was placed on food production and on the home economics side, largely canning.

"The program started in the schools and much credit for the early development of the program must be given to county school superintendents, rural teachers, and various business firms including many newspapers.

"After the war a national leaders' meeting in Kansas City resulted in establishing the needs of a lasting program. And a foundation was laid for:

1. *A local club organization which would be independent of the schools.*

2. *Local self determination of club.*

3. *Community, state, and national cooperatives.*

4. *A program with educational value designed to fit the ability and needs of the youth.*

"Thus, the basis was laid for the development of a youth program which concerned itself with the personal development of the member. Emphasis has changed from the cow or calf or the blue ribbon to the boy or girl. Projects are considered the useful tasks by which youth are now challenged, and the medium through which their solid growth occurs.

"Projects are a means to an end . . . not an end in themselves. One could say that the end purpose of all 4-H work now is development of the individual's character, knowledge and skills so he or she can lead a richer and fuller life and more ably meet the responsibilities of a democratic society."[23]

Christened "4-H"

In 1927 Boys and Girls Club work officially became 4-H Club work. This change in name and directions came out of the National Club Leaders' Conference in June at the First National Club Camp in Washington, D. C., with the U. S. Department of Agriculture and the Land-Grant Colleges cooperating.

The National Club pledge, emblem, motto, and slogan were adopted as now used in the United States. In due time the "ear-marks" of club work were so designated and protected by a Congressional resolution for the exclusive use of 4-H clubs of the United States. The emblem on the national pin was further protected by a patent, held in trust by the U. S. Department of Agriculture.

A committee of state club leaders was appointed prior to this conference to work cooperatively with the U. S. Department of Agriculture in reviewing the

[23]Charline Lindsay, *Significant Changes in the Missouri 4-H Program,* (Columbia, Missouri, University of Missouri, Extension Service, Staff Member in a special unpublished paper, 1968), P. 1-2.

status of these club symbols. The Committee consisted of T. T. Martin, Missouri, Chairman; G. L. Farley, Massachusetts, Secretary; and W. J. Jernigan, Arkansas.

Consideration was first given to the symbols then used by all states. By way of illustration, the pledge of each state was studied. Then, the form which was more nearly like the pledge of the majority of the states was recommended. Finally, this recommended form was further changed and adopted.

The Missouri 4-H Club pledge was like the pledge adopted, except it had the phrase, "As a true club member, I pledge . . . " Kansas is credited with originating the National Club Pledge.

During the 1930's many club leaders expressed dissatisfaction with the prevailing small project unit of club organization. After all viewpoints had been considered the judgment of the Cooperative Extension Service was interpreted to mean about the following:

a. Enlarging the units of community or neighborhood organization was favored. According to this plan, all members of project clubs of the same locality would be offered the opportunity to form one larger club, with project units. New clubs were encouraged to start on the "larger organization" basis.

b. This natural unit of operation increased the interest of more members by providing a wider variety of both projects and group activities. It also enabled such enlarged groups to take part in larger social and recreational activities. In addition, the mature and experienced members often could carry larger responsibilities, such as more than one project, junior leadership, and committee work.

It was observed further that when a member was challenged to work to his capacity, he remained a club member longer. Another apparent advantage was that more in-service training and work of leaders was possible. The over-all results were more community cooperation, larger club events, and more publicity for club achievements.

This change to the community 4-H club unit of organization closed the so-called third period of club work in Missouri.

The Community 4-H Club Organization

The next significant development in the program had its beginning in 1938, when, for the first time the community type club was organized. Previous to this time only a limited number of clubs were continuous in operation and all members of a given club were enrolled in the same project. Many times in a given community there would be three or four or even more different clubs with interlocking membership. The change to the community type continuous organization, beginning in the late 30's, developed slowly but gradually, until this became the prevailing type of club in the mid 40's.

By 1950 practically all clubs in Missouri were organized on the community type plan. In this plan all members in a community belonged to the same club. They then divided into smaller or satellite groups for project work. This called for more leadership and made possible larger clubs. More important, the clubs became more continuous and were able to expand their program more effectively, including such things as recreation, safety, wildlife conservation, health, grooming, community service, and other activities. This brought into being the second major section of club work, that of group work.

Group work opened up many new opportunities for the personal development of the individual boys and girls. Even though it is not as well known as project work, it is equally important in the development of the individual. As club members work together in their monthly club meetings they select one of the subjects that the club will work on together during the year, and this is called the 4-H club activity. There are many positive results from the 4-H activity. First, it broadens the knowledge of the boy and girl. Activity brings more new subject matter to the 4-H members and the learning process is stimulated by group participation.

Second, it teaches cooperation. Through group work members must make plans together to carry out a program which includes participation on committees, taking part in programs, working out problems, and sharing responsibility together. All of this contributes to their attitude of cooperation.

A youth group such as 4-H can do much to teach young people to take as well as to give and to build attitudes toward accepting others with their weak and strong points, and to work together to accomplish things that can be achieved in no other way.

Third is consideration of others. Many of the community service activities do a wonderful job of teaching young people to be civic minded, to be concerned about things and people around them. It teaches them to be concerned not only for the local community but also for the state and nation and world about them. This may seem a lofty idea for a 10-year-old. Remember the seeds of consideration are sown at home in the community club and school.

The fourth is social adjustment which comes through participation in a group. Club work provides opportunities for boys and girls to plan to work and to play together which is a necessary part of growing up.

Leadership development is a natural in group work in 4-H. The member is reaching out for opportunities in leadership and through club activities the members have opportunities to take part on committees and make plans, organize programs, and stand before a group, perhaps for the first time, to express themselves.

Impact of These on the Community Club

Some results achieved because of this larger unit of club organization, according to annual reports of the Extension Service, include the following:

a. The new community type of organization developed all over the state. It was started largely in 1938. However, there were still a few school clubs and many project groups being conducted. R. H. Emberson organized and helped to conduct school clubs in non-agent counties until his death at 80 years of age, on December 30, 1942.

b. It took more than five years for the Missouri Cooperative Extension Service to revise and adapt club literature and reports, and to change leader training methods to fit the new system.

c. All-year-around clubs became more practical. The larger organization unit was more elastic and adaptable to interests and needs of club members at all times of the year.

In the early forties, several adaptations of 4-H were made because of war. They included:

a. Production quotas were set up and the National Mobilization Week of April 4-11, 1942, was observed.

b. Projects which emphasized food, fiber, fats, and scrap metal drives were given priority. Health, first aid, and home nursing were in second place.

c. Father and son partnerships were endorsed but little was accomplished in Missouri in this area.

d. Missouri tried without success to follow through with the national plan of mobilization for non-farm youth. Such youth were to receive pay for their farm labors and be given a "Victory" pin for completing 200 hours of labor on farms.

Now as suburban and urban clubs were developing, vacation time clubs with single projects were finding some favor. This was not regarded as a step backward but rather an adjustment to meet a particular situation or need.

The first leader's guide for voluntary project leaders came into use along with the community type club. Soon after a leader's guide became standard equipment for all except the most advanced project members who rely primarily on member initiative and counseling with leaders and agents.

During the forties much training of voluntary leaders was done by specialists. During the fifties the specialists gradually moved to working with county staff, and agents took over the voluntary leader training function.

Standards Adopted

As club work progressed in America each state adopted certain rules, and patterned them for their own Extension Service situation. In the main these club requirements are the same in each state. As a general rule, in the earlier periods more stress was placed upon contests and less on democratic procedures. Later this balance was to change.

A conference was held at Kansas City in 1918, by the U. S. Department of Agriculture and the Land-Grant Colleges.

This conference adopted the first Standard Club Requirements for this section of the United States as follows: Each club must,

1. Have a membership of at least five in the same project with members 10 to 21 years of age.

2. Have a local club leader throughout the year.

3. Have a local club organization with officers and a constitution.

4. Have a definite club program for the entire year.

5. Hold at least six regular meetings during the year, with a secretary to keep records of the meetings and of the progress of each member.

6. Conduct a local exhibit annually.

7. Have a club demonstration team to give at least one public demonstration in the home community.

8. At least 50 percent of the members complete their project. work and present a report to the county or state leader.

9. Have a judging team chosen by competition.

10. Hold an achievement program on completion of work.

11. Hold membership in the Farm Bureau or other county extension organization.

When the first four requirements were met, a charter signed by the U. S. Secretary of Agriculture, the State Director, and the State Club Leader was granted. When all the requirements were met in a single year, the club received a Seal of Achievement.

Silver, Gold, and Blue Ribbon Seal Clubs

In Missouri, a club charter is issued to a Standard 4-H Club upon completion of organization.

Upon completion of the year's work, applications are made for recognition. Of the 1740 clubs of 1963, 742, or 43 percent, merited the Blue Ribbon Seal. These clubs were evaluated by the following standard:

Standard for a Silver Seal Club

The Silver Seal Club must have:

1. Five or more members.

2. A full set of officers.

3. A club leader and necessary project leaders.

4. Six or more regular monthly meetings.

5. At least one project group of five or more members.

6. Health and recreation included in the club program.

7. A local achievement program or participation in a county achievement program.

8. Seventy-five percent of the members completing.

Standard for a Gold Seal Club

A Gold Seal Club must have:

1. Eight or more members.

2. A full set of officers.

3. A club leader and necessary project leaders.

4. Ten or more regular monthly club meetings.

5. At least one project group with five or more members.

YOUTH WITH 4-H BACKGROUND LOOKS CONFIDENTLY TO THE FUTURE.
Darrel Davison, Adair County, and Leona Sue Santee, Barry County, were featured in this picture appearing on the cover of the 1961 4-H Foundation brochure.

Members of the Oak Grove Club in Buchanan County, the first Missouri girls 4-H Club on record, are pictured in 1916: Clara Knapp, Dixie Doan, Lillie Joss, Edith Pixler, Esther Knapp, and Ida Roup, leader.

A three generation picture of members of the Oak Grove Club: Mrs. Cornelia Knapp Castle, leader, right front row; Mrs. Esther Knapp Archdekin, left back row; first generation member; Frank Archdekin, Sr., back row center, second generation; Frank Archdekin, Jr., back row right; and Patrick Archdekin, front center, third generation. Mrs. Frank Archdekin is the mother of Frank and Patrick.

The 747 delegates to the 1947 State 4-H Club Week posed for this emblem picture. One hundred counties are represented.

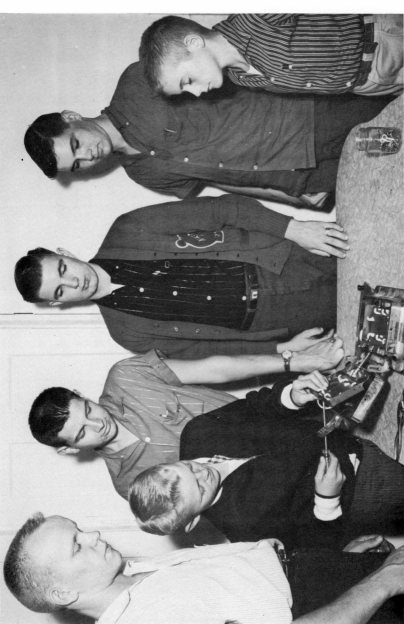

Illustrating a project group within a community club structure is this 4-H electricity project group in Adair County. Edmund Polovich, the demonstrator, a national 4-H scholarship winner in electricity in 1958, is now leading a 4-H electricity project.

FOUR-H YOUTH HAVE THE ENTHUSIASTIC BACKING OF ADULTS...
(R. V. Duncan, left, president of the Iowa-Missouri Walnut Co., St. Joseph, sponsored trips to National 4-H Conference for many years. One of the delegates, Eddie Turner, Buchanan County, is pictured with him. After, Mr. Duncan's death in 1959, his son, Dan, continued the sponsorship.)

. . . AND THE ENDORSEMENT OF LEADERS OF OUR NATION.
(President Dwight D. Eisenhower greeting 1957 National 4-H Club Congress dele-
gation.)

Typical 4-H Club meeting of the Lathrop Club in Clinton County, 1947. James Chenoweth, president; Mrs. Earl Daniels and Cecil Hays, leaders.

6.　A minimum of six project meetings (a total of all projects), in addition to the regular monthly club meetings.

7.　A planned program for regular monthly meetings including project demonstrations, health, recreation, and an elective 4-H activity.

8.　A local achievement program or participation in a county achievement program.

9.　Participation of adult leaders in county council meetings and leader training meetings.

10.　Eighty percent of the members completing.

Standard for a Blue Ribbon Seal Club

A Blue Ribbon Seal Club must have:

1.　Ten or more members.

2.　A full set of officers.

3.　A club leader and necessary project leaders.

4.　Twelve or more regular monthly meetings—two of which may be social meetings.

5.　Planned programs for the regular monthly meetings.

6.　Achieve one or more goals in recreation, health, and one additional 4-H activity.

7.　A local achievement program or participation in a county achievement program.

8.　Participation of adult leaders in county council meetings and leader training meetings.

9.　Eighty-five percent of members completing.

Clubs With Long Histories

Certain clubs in Missouri's long club history may be sorted out as progress pacesetters. Certain clubs, many of which existed prior to designation as 4-H clubs, developed programs of excellence, established records in continuity, or blazed new trails and thereby contributed to the progress that gives modern day clubs a rich heritage.

It is not possible to give credit to all deserving clubs in this historical sketch. A few are mentioned here as examples.

As stated before, the first clubs of record in Missouri were organized in Iron County in April, 1914. A corn club with seven members under the leadership of B. P. Burnham was established at Ironton. The other corn club had eight or nine members. Melvin J. Kelly was the leader. It was organized in the King School just East of Annapolis. Frank Morris, who is still living in Iron County, was a member of the club near Annapolis. Active in that club's work also was one of the teachers, J. L. Hickman.

It is difficult to establish continuity in clubs. For example, an area in Jackson County, embracing two school districts—Dekalb and Oldham—had at one time seven clubs. Many of these date far back into the 1920's. Sometime in the 1940's all of these clubs were merged into one community type club—The Independence Pioneers Club. It drew on an area larger than the original two districts and grew to be a club of more than 100 members and often a completion record of more than 90 percent. This has been the history of many of the early clubs. A few, however, as we shall see, maintained the original project club and grew into community clubs.

There is briefly presented on the following pages the stories of some of the clubs in various counties of the state that played an important role in early 4-H development.

Atchison County

Boys and girls club work in Atchison County in 1919 was limited to several hot lunch clubs in rural schools, and one calf club organized just east of Fairfax. The calf club was known as the Atchison County Calf Club. Club leader was George Pettyman, and the county agent at the time was the late J. M. Slaughter.

What is now the St. Joseph Interstate Baby Beef and Pig Show was started in 1920. Lois Barlow, now Mrs. Warren Chambers, of the Fairfax Club, showed the grand champion calf at the first Interstate Show. The animal sold for $75 per hundred, which was a record price at that time. The calf cost $36.30 and was fed for 173 days. It weighed 1,080 pounds at the time of the sale. Lois Barlow also had the reserve champion calf in 1921.

Lois was awarded a trip to the International Livestock Show at Chicago in 1920 by Armour & Company. Other delegates from Missouri to the International that year were Lee Steen of Sturges, and Charles Steele of Chillicothe.

Lois used the money from her prize winnings in 1920 and 1921 to finance her college education at Northwest State Teachers College.

Other members of the Calf Club in 1920 included Marvin Barlow, Leon Barlow, Loren Heard, Ethan Allen Poe, Evelyn Poe, Myrtle Curry, Harvey Wilson, James Sillers, P. A. Sillers, James Wilson, Wilma Green, Russel New, Joe New, Loren Lininger, Dale Lininger, Kenneth Lininger, James Moody, and Raymond Grash.

The Farmer's City Club began in 1922, when a boys and girls club was formed at the Farmer's City Bank Building in Westboro, Missouri. During the period 1919-1922, there was a County Baby Beef Club, a County Pig Club, and a County Corn Club. Several members from the Farmer's City neighborhood were members of these clubs, though a list of members is not available at this time.

The boys and girls clubs in Westboro moved to the Yale School in 1924. The Farmer's City Sow & Litter Club was started in 1926. This was apparently the first club to have the Farmer's City name. Members of the first Farmer's City Club were Albert Rolf, Lee Broermann, Marvin Barlow, Allen Barlow, Jr., and Ruth Klute. Allen Barlow, Sr., was the leader, and George Prettyman was the county leader since there was no county agent at that time.

The Farmer's City Community Club was issued a charter in 1939. This was the year when the community clubs were started in Missouri. Charles Broermann was recognized for 18 years service in 1941. In 1946 Mr. Broermann was awarded a trip to State 4-H Week in Columbia for being the leader of one of the 100 best clubs in the state. Mr. Broermann was honored at his home in 1953 with a surprise dinner and program in which many former 4-H members recited their 4-H experiences under his leadership. He had been a leader for three decades at this time.

In 1943, Duane Broermann, of the Farmer's City Club, sold his calf at the St. Joseph Interstate War Bond auction for $600,000. This calf was chosen from the Farmer's City group because that club had shown more years consistently than any other club exhibiting at the St. Joseph Show. The calf was purchased from Duane by a committee of businessmen represented by Harry Garlock of the St. Joseph Stockyards Company. It was sold in the auction to the Wyeth Hardware Company.

Harry Broermann, Charles Broermann's son, attended National 4-H Club Camp in Washington, D. C., in 1935 and the National 4-H Club Congress in Chicago in 1936.

In 1953, Carolyn Butt of the Farmer's City Club was IFYE delegate to Puerto Rico. Carmen Burgos of Puerto Rico was the exchange delegate to Atchison County that year.

Buchanan County

The Oak Grove 4-H Club in Buchanan County has been in existence for most of the 50 years (1914-1964). It had its beginning as a group of girls who were taught domestic science in 1913.

The teacher at that time was Miss Nellie Sweeney. This group of girls became a club in October, 1914. It is the first girls club of record in Missouri. There were seven members: Esther Knapp, now Mrs. Sam Archdekin; Bertha Knapp, now Mrs. Harry Miller; Lorena Gradert, now Mrs. Howard Hall; Leona Gradert, now Mrs. John Karrle; Edith Pixler, now Mrs. Curtis Shreeves; Goldie Smith, now Mrs. R. H. Robertson; Helen Miller, now Mrs. E. Nunnenkempt; Lillie Joss became Mrs. Howard Roach and died in 1957; and Dixie Doane, now Mrs. Lewis Brown.

Cornelia Knapp, a sister of Esther and Bertha, now Mrs. J. Blaine Castle, served as leader all the years 1914-1919, except for the year 1916 when she was away attending school at Maryville. Ida Roup (Johnson) was leader that year. Clara Knapp, the youngest of the Knapp sisters, became of eligible age and joined the club in 1916.

Clothing and canning appeared to have been the leading projects during the years listed here.

Credit for organizing goes to the Oak Grove Home Makers Club, organized October 21, 1913. Miss Bab Bell of the state Extension staff helped to organize it. Mrs. Paul Kabus was president, Mrs. Frank Knapp, vice-president, and Mrs. J.H. Maupin secretary. The club is still active.

In 1924, County Home Agent Margaret C. Huston helped to organize four girls clubs at Easton, Pickett, Riverside, and Oak Grove in Buchanan County. Riverside has been absorbed by the 102 Club but the three other clubs still exist in Buchanan County under the original names.

"Nine girls enrolled in Garment Making I in the Oak Grove Club in 1924 with Mrs. H. Grable as the other leader. The next year there were three projects—Clothing I, II, and Young Housekeepers with 16 enrolled. Supper, dinner, meal planning, baking, canning, poultry, dairy, garden, and more attractive home projects were the club's program through the years until 1939, with 33 being the highest membership of any year. In 1939, its fifteenth year, the Oak Grove Club was organized on the community basis with 10 girls enrolled and 5 projects offered.

"From 1924 through 1960 there have been 8 who attended Club Congress, two other trip winners had done practically all their club work in this club before they moved away, and four have attended the National 4-H Conference in Washington, D. C. Nine demonstrations have reached state level and seven were awarded blue ribbons. Ten members have competed in dairy judging at the state level. Five others have had top scores in five different state judging contests. Perhaps the real test of the Oak Grove Club's value is that in 1961, 10 members are of the second generation. There have been 236 individual members from 146 families. In all, 19 are or have been second generation members."

Another Oak Grove Club charter member, Mrs. Anita Washburn, whose maiden name was Anita Zogrodsky, said in 1961:

"Aware of the needs of farm youth, the Oak Grove Club has provided the good leadership necessary to maintain an active 4-H club for some 37 years. Prominent among those who have served as project or community leaders has been Miss Ione Jones, who was leader of the first club and has continued to work with 4-H members these many years.

"Just as it would be difficult to evaluate the training and knowledge received by these young people, it is difficult to summarize the awards and honors that have been achieved. Prior to 1939, there were four demonstration teams that placed first in the state. Other honors include: four members who have represented Missouri at the National 4-H Club Camp in Washington, D. C.: Nellie Mable Jones Turner-1927; Anita Zogrodsky Washburn-1930; and Edwin S. Turner (son of Nellie Mable)-1959. (Since this was written a second member of the Jones family, Joan Turner, 1963, should be added to the list of 4-H Club National Conference delegates.)

"The top award or honor, if there was one, should go to Miss Ione Jones, whose faithful and capable leadership has, indeed, been a blessing to the Oak Grove Community. Many others have served or assisted with club work, but her service has been consistent and of very long standing. Along with her, the members of her family have shared her keen interest in 4-H Club activities. Miss Jones and her family have done much to keep the Oak Grove 4-H Club an active one—instructive, productive, and ever striving to 'make the best better'."

Cole County

A club was organized in Cole County in 1919 with 16 members. The Mayor of Jefferson City, the Commercial Club, and C. G. Leuker, county agent, imported 48 Holstein and Jersey heifers from Wisconsin.

In 1927 Otto Pitrick led a corn club at Russellville. There were seven members. The highest yields of 79 bushels per acre were made by Hugo and Alvin Raithel. The club held an Achievement Day on November 11. In the evening five reels of motion pictures were shown. There was a full house. Each boy exhibited 10 ears of corn.

Greene County

Mrs. J. N. Morton was the leader of the Pollyanna Club in Greene County. She was the leader of a demonstration team to the Sioux City Interstate Fair in

1922. Opal Sherrill, now Mrs. Opal Louizader, and Catherine McKee, now Mrs. Jas. E. O'Bryan, composed the team. The club existed for seven years, during which time three mothers of members died and the girls took over the homemaking. Their 4-H training and Mrs. Morton's counsel were invaluable to them.

All of the "Pollyanna's" got together in 1959 and helped the Mortons celebrate their golden wedding. C. C. Keller, who served Greene County as a county agent and who was on duty at the time this club was active, was among those present. There was much reminiscing.

Springfield, county seat of Greene County, is the center of one of the largest dairy industries in the United States. Entries in the 4-H dairy classes at the Ozark Empire Fair at Springfield rival and often exceed those at the State Fair. The dairy project has had a prominent place in the 4-H program of Greene County for many years.

Mrs. Robert Hawkins and Mrs. Tom Whiteside were leaders in a county-wide dairy project in the early years of club work. Later Mrs. Robert Thompson, Mrs. Ben Edmonson, and Mrs. Maude Ingram gave many years to club leadership. In the days when the National Dairy Show and the Dairy Cattle Congress at Waterloo, Iowa, made a place for 4-H demonstration contests, Greene County was usually a contender and was sometimes a winner of this state honor. Joe Edmonson, now dairy department chairman at the University of Missouri - Columbia, and Alvin Laughlin represented Missouri in Waterloo in 1934. Joe Edmonson was a delegate to the National Camp in 1937.

Jackson County

In 1915, E. A. Ikenberry and Jackson County Superintendent of Schools Blackburn, planned and held, with the help of local people, township festivals in seven townships. A wide variety of articles was exhibited. Standards in that early day for classifying and judging were indefinite. There was wide participation and much enthusiasm. A young farmer, Harry S. Truman, who took pride in his straight furrows, was superintendent of the Grandview Township Festival.

The Six Mile Baby Beef Club of Jackson County was organized in 1927 with George Koger as leader. From its beginning it was a year around, twelve-month club. It held its annual meeting each year in December, carried wildlife conservation and music appreciation as activities, and was in fact, a community type of club 10 years in advance of the state's adoption of this idea.

In its first 11 years this club had seven of its members selected as delegates to the National 4-H Club Camp (now Conference) in Washington, D. C. It is believed that this is a record for a single club. Mr. Koger was leader for 10 years.

Lutie Chiles was a delegate to the second National Camp in 1928, Lorene Hostetter and Billy Winfrey both attended the third National Camp in 1929. Others were Irvin Brune, Marguerite Ferguson, Fred Brune, and Roy Lentz. Later Mary Jean Lentz brought this club's all-time record to eight National delegates from among its members.

Jefferson County

A dairy club with 14 members was organized in October, 1922, in the Ware Community in Jefferson County. E. T. Itschner was county agent and organizer. He later became state Extension dairy specialist. Adolph Eaton was the local leader.

Three members of this club: Jack Cornell, Lloyd Huskey, and Adelbert Cornell, composed the dairy judging team that won the state contest at the Missouri State Fair at Sedalia in 1923. The team placed ninth that year in the National 4-H Dairy Judging Contest at Syracuse, New York, with Jack Cornell placing third out of 66 boys competing from 22 states.

This, according to Cannon C. Hearne, later on the state Extension staff in Columbia, in a news story published in 1925, started a chain of events that resulted in $12,000 additional income for the Ware Community that year.

Johnson County

The Home Improvement League was organized in Johnson County in 1913 for the purpose of improving the community socially. It was the result of a domestic science school held by a Miss Nesbit or a Miss Bell. Mrs. J. P. Hutchison of Elm reported at the time of the club's organization: "The main effort of the club is to render the home more attractive to the boys and girls and to make the home more convenient."

The Pittsville Home Improvement Club organized a tomato club with eight members and several organized sewing societies for girls. Mrs. Ivan Phillips was President of the Township League and Ruth Ballard made the first report.

The Missouri Homemakers Conference was organized in 1908 at Farmers Week. The first County Homemakers Club that grew out of this conference was started by Mrs. Harry Sneed of Pettis County in 1912. Mrs. Sneed initiated the idea of a county worker for women, a forerunner of the home demonstration agent. Miss Mildred E. Hinton, called the "Soup Lady", carried on a program featuring hot lunches for school chilren. She had a status comparable to that of Sam Jordan before his official designation as county agent of Pettis County.

It should be borne in mind that before 1914 no pattern existed for a club organization. There were no project descriptions, no literature, no standards, no requirements, no records, no demonstrating, no judging—all of these things had to be "built in" as time moved on.

Twenty-five members were enrolled in the Centerview Pig Club in 1920. The Bank of Centerview bought 20 registered Duroc and five Poland China gilts. They were distributed to the boys and girls on June 12. Members drew numbers out of a hat for order of choice. Jim Eppright got 20th choice of the 20 Durocs but his animal placed first in its class at the show in the fall. Chester Jacoby showed the blue-ribbon Poland China.

C. B. Hoover was leader of a beef heifer club of 19 members which began in 1921. These Jackson Township young people bought registered Shorthorn and Hereford heifers and sold them at a show and sale in April, 1922. W. A. Cochel, famous in Shorthorn circles, judged. This was a very active club that featured tours and judging.

Forty-six were members of a dairy county-wide club in 1921. A carload of young Holstein calves was shipped from Wisconsin, but seven died enroute. About half were retained on the farms; others were sold at auction the following year.

Lafayette County

The Alma 4-H Club in Lafayette County has been in continuous existence for 25 years. It started as a Health and Happiness Club in 1936, under the leadership of

Mrs. J. H. Nolte, who has been leading various clubs since 1942. Mrs. Ernie Brockman became leader in 1938 and continued as a leader for 23 years.

Lawrence County

More than 100 boys and girls were enrolled in purebred pig projects in 1921 in Lawrence County. Veteran breeders said the classes shown by youth in the autumn of 1921 were the best they had ever seen. Purebred swine and dairy cattle were established on 100 farms that first year.

Linn County

Linn County had 41 members in a purebred gilt club in 1920 and 55 members in 1921. A purebred Hereford heifer club of 10 members was organized in 1920. R. G. Shouse and L. H. Edens were leaders, and Ross Nichols was county agent.

Madison County

Madison County's 4-H record goes back more than 40 years. Dorothy Stucky, now Mrs. E. A. Truman, leader of the German 4-H Club in 1960, was winner of a trip to Columbia, having produced the best coop of chickens at the county fair in Fredericktown in 1920. Mrs. Will Kessler was leader at that time. Ruth Schulte, now Mrs. Paul Skaggs, was a member of the Village Creek Club at that time under the leadership of Mrs. Elizabeth Blanton.

McDonald County

The Needles Eye 4-H Club of Anderson, first led by Mrs. Dewey Cole, has served the community for 26 years. The community leader for 1960 and 1961 was Ron Selney, Missouri Highway Patrolman.

Newton County

Mrs. Mildred Snider of the Sware Prairie 4-H Club reported: "The Sware Prairie 4-H Club was started in 1926 as a sewing club with Mrs. Nina Kellhoffer and Mrs. Ola Lawson as leaders. Then poultry was added as a project and the club was called Hickory Grove Community Club. Projects have been: health in 1931, bees in 1933, forestry in 1936 and soil conservation in 1937. Many boys and girls in this club won blue ribbons and gold awards in county, district, and state meetings."

From 1931 to 1946, Avis, Marcellene and Betty Lou Lankford won blue ribbons and several trips to Columbia and the state meetings. There they also won blue ribbons in clothing and food preservation projects.

In 1939, Avis Lankford won the state health award and a trip to Chicago to the National 4-H Club Congress. In 1941, Marcellene Lankford represented Missouri at the National 4-H Club Camp for outstanding club work. Betty Lou Lankford won a $150 scholarship to the University of Missouri in 1946.

Ruth and Beulah Markel also won blue ribbons and awards for food preservation projects.

In 1936, the forestry team made up of Elva and Jack Kellhoffer, won first place with a forestry demonstration at the Missouri State Round-Up. In 1937 Elva Kellhoffer and Lyndall Mailes presented an outstanding demonstration on soil conservation. They won a blue ribbon at the State Round-Up. Elva Kellhoffer was selected as an "outstanding club member", and had a place in the candle lighting service. Albert Rinehart won a registered Jersey heifer as a prize on an essay he wrote: "Why I Should Win This Calf." He won several blue ribbons and awards with this heifer in county, district, state and national meetings. The heifer became foundation cow for a herd of Jersey cattle.

The Cedar Creek Club of Newton County has had an uninterrupted existence since 1929 when Mrs. H. E. Clements led a clothing club. It has been a community club since 1947 with Mrs. L. E. Becknell as its first community leader. The Cedar Creek Club has for many years been outstanding in wildlife conservation. The Lloyd Hickman family has had a prominent place in the 4-H program in Newton County for many years.

Oregon County

Mrs. Ambie Eckhard was designated "4-H Pioneer" of Oregon County in 1926 by T. T. Martin, then State 4-H Leader. Here is a part of her story in her own words. "I think the first 4-H club was organized in 1924. A Mr. Russell, a minister, came to Thayer and organized a 4-H club. I don't think he completed it, but left. Gretchen Frommel Gahn was a member. He gave me information on how to organize a club so it was a case of the 'blind leading the blind'. I organized and led three clubs that year. We did not complete the tomato club because of the drought. This was the only one I failed to complete in the 19 I led. Each club repeated for several years. My four-year-old baby boy would ride in the saddle with me to meetings when I couldn't make it in the old Model "T" Ford car. Soon I was organizing clubs in neighboring communities. When J. R. Paulling became county agent, interest in 4-H Club work was greatly increased."

The club projects while Mr. Paulling was county agent included: clothing, health and first aid, canning, home furnishings, sheep, pig, kaffir, and soybeans. Some of the early club members in Oregon County were: Dorothy Hertzler Manker; Estella Hertzler Hooper; Mary, Jeanie, and Victor Barnella; Helen Carlock; Myrtle Ary, Joe and Howard Eckard.

Pemiscot County

In 1926, Mrs. Albert Ball of Pemiscot County walked nearly a mile twice a month to club meetings, carrying her baby and her books. Mrs. Ball, at the age of 31, was the mother of eight children; the oldest was seventeen. She and her eleven-months-old baby, Margaret, attended Farmer's Week at Columbia in 1927. A feature article published at the time said that she was a "picture of health and happiness."

Pettis County

One of the earliest club members in this county was Mrs. Paul Read, whose maiden name was Anna M. Close. Ten girls in the Cottage Grove community were in this club. Mrs. Read had been active as a 4-H leader and has served the program in many ways. She wrote and produced a 4-H play. It was given at one of the evening programs at Farmer's Week in Jesse Auditorium at the University of Missouri - Columbia.

As early as 1915, C. M. Long, Pettis County agent, reported 46 clubs with a membership of 256. Mr. Long started dairy project work. In December, 1921, under the leadership of W. T. Angle, 133 registered gilts were distributed to club boys and girls. This breeding stock had a great influence in improving the hog industry of the county. Norton Heffernan of the Maplewood community, and Raymond Kahrs and Raymond Klien of the Smithton Club made excellent records with their sow and litter projects.

The community with the unusual name of "Striped College" has had a 4-H club since 1928 when E. C. Stevens, the father of nine children, organized and led a corn club with 10 members. A school building gave this community its interesting name. It was built like a box, with white pine boards nailed bottom to top. It was striped with blue battens. Striped College, in the early 1960's, had a community club with 61 members.

Estell Jenkins, now Mrs. Ellis, was president of the Cartwright Club of ten members in 1924. This club was active in 4-H State Fair events in the early twenties. Mrs. Ellis has been an outstanding leader for many years.

A girls' club in the Quisenberry Community developed parliamentary procedure to a high state of perfection in 1923. Elizabeth James, as president, was almost a "ritual specialist."

As evidence of early voluntary leader support, the Maplewood community on one occasion honored twenty-four 4-H leaders. They were:

Mrs. Ed Heffernan	*Mrs. Norton Heffernan*
Mrs. Frank Barrick	*Mr. Norton Heffernan*
Mrs. Ann Franklin Scott	*Mr. M. C. Ford*
Mr. Walter Rissler	*Mr. John Bennett*
Mrs. Walter Rissler	*Mrs. John Bennett*
Mrs. Walter Banning	*Mrs. John Harris*
Mrs. William Williams	*Mrs. John Sutherland*
Mrs. Carl Landes	*Mrs. Dorothy Helen Van Orman*
Mr. James Ellis	*Mr. John Rundlett*
Mrs. James Ellis	*Mrs. John Rundlett*
Mrs. E. Cusick	*Alice Rissler - Ass't Leader*
Mrs. Margaret Longan	*Buddy Williams*

The Dresden 4-H Community Club in recent years is considered a typical club, maintaining a membership near 20. It represents a consolidation of many project clubs, starting in 1925. H. L. Bolton was the leader of a corn club. The 4-H corn judging team that year was Paul Gottschalk, August Hintz (later pastor of a Chicago church), and Junior Ferguson. Anna Cathrine Romig and Ruth Rene represented Missouri in poultry judging at the National Poultry Congress in Cleveland, Ohio. Eddie Good, a poultry club member, lost his life in World War II.

John Elmer Fichter, a poultry club member, is now soils specialist for the Soil Conservation Service of Missouri.

Ralph Romig graduated from the Missouri College of Agriculture, and was county agent for a time. He is now a farmer and livestock breeder in Perry County.

Commendable records were made in baby beef, clothing, home grounds, and gardening in addition to those mentioned.

Other active Pettis County leaders include: Mr. C. E. Ferguson, Mrs. George Fichter, Mrs. Oscar Kemp, Mrs. Bruce Richey, and Mrs. L. W. Raabe.

Since the formation of a community club, the leaders have been: Mrs. C. E. Ferguson, Mrs. Bruce Richey, Mrs. Standley Woodward, Mrs. M. K. Tunstall, and Mrs. Dennis Raabe.

Platte County

Seventy-seven Poland (both black and spotted) gilts were distributed in Platte County in 1921. Breed association committees inspected the litters and tagged those in their judgment qualified for registry. Some 260 out of a total of 450 were tagged. Eighty-nine were added from 150 applicants in 1922. E. L. Dolan, N. L. Farmer, R. S. Clemens, J. J. Wills, W. A. Porter and Coin M. Morton were the promoters of this fine program.

St. Charles County

At the early State Round-Ups (the first was held in 1928), the St. Charles County delegation was one of the largest and most active. They commanded attention in appearance with uniform dress and two men in charge, George Karston, music teacher and local leader, and R. A. Langenbaecher, county agent.

Participation included a county chorus. For years county choruses were recognized. Mr. Langenbaecher claims that Miss Mattie O'Fallon of the Cottleville Community was the number one 4-H leader of the county in the early years. Her sister, Susie O'Fallon, is also listed as an outstanding leader. Mrs. Walter Faeth, whose maiden name was Marie Karston, and her family have been very active in 4-H Club work for many years.

St. Charles County did some pioneering in camping, starting in 1923. Mr. Langenbaecher, county agent, says about that: "We slept the 'flock' on blankets of straw. Had an eight-foot canvas partition between the boys and girls. The little devils kept us leaders busy keeping them from needling the other side".

St. Charles County has continued its camping program for 38 years. Camping facilities are used at Sherwood Forest in Cuivre River State Park. This was originally a demonstration camping area and it adheres to high camping standards.

Wayne Short was a delegate to the second National 4-H Camp (now National 4-H Conference) in 1928. His earnings from his registered Poland China hogs enabled him to graduate from Central College at Fayette, Missouri. He is now an official in the National Audubon Society.

In more recent years, Janice Jungerman has made outstanding contributions as a member and a leader.

St. Louis County

Three active clubs in St. Louis County have been in continuous existence for 34 years. All were organized in 1937. The Goldwater-Brown Club had seven members its first year. Mrs. Tess Porter was the leader, and Hilda Albers was the first president. She later served as leader for 22 years.

Mrs. George Weinreich was the first leader of the Oakville Club. Herb Fink, a delegate to the National Camp in 1928, was a member of the Chesterfield Club.

In 1960, enrollments in these three clubs were:

Goldwater-Brown . . . . 15 members
Oaksville . . . . 70 members
Chesterfield . . . . .14 members.

Ray County

The following is from a 1929 Ray County Report:

"The Egypt Bottom Potato Club begun in 1924, under the leadership of F. D. Stonner, has brought not only distinction to Ray County but to the entire State of Missouri. Members of the club this year each grew at least one-half acre of potatoes under the direction of the local leader and under methods recommended by the Missouri College of Agriculture, and in consequence produced some of the highest yields secured in the potato district.

"In addition, the club members prepared a demonstration showing the principles which they used in their potato club work. They presented it at picnics and other places in the county to growers interested in improved potato cultural methods. They packed their material and samples of their potatoes into a truck and went to the State Fair, where they were awarded blue ribbon honors for their demonstrations, and second for their potato display.

"A team of boys from this club represented Missouri at the Interstate Fair at Sioux City and won second place with their demonstration.

"The Central Community Pig Club this year has been a demonstration of the value of local leadership and club training. Due to the resignation of Joe Shirky, the local leader, because of sickness, Roy Nicholson, who had been a club member five years, was named to succeed Shirky. He visited the six rural schools of the community and enrolled eight members. He saw that they were supplied with purebred sows and gave careful instructions in the care of pigs. He was responsible for the local meeting of the club and had much to do with arranging for the local pig club show held for the purpose of selecting the hogs to represent the club at the Missouri State Fair at Sedalia. He also encouraged the judging team and assisted it in its studies. He had the team members on hand whenever the county leader was present for instruction.

"Members of this club made creditable exhibits at theState Fair and won first place in the State Judging Contest. Roy Nicholson also won first place in the State 4-H Club Leader Contest. He also helped prepare the judging team for the Interstate Fair at Sioux City and the American Royal at Kansas City. He was a delegate to National Club Camp in 1928."

*   *   *

This story of Missouri 4-H Club work now moves into one of the most interesting periods of the State and Nation's history—the period so often referred to as "The Twenties." These were the days of low farm prices immediately following World War I, but it also was a period of world peace.

Chapter IV

THE PROGRAM

Projects . . . . Activities . . . . Methods

During the decade from 1920 to 1930 the Cooperative Extension Service emerged from a concept, authorized in the Smith-Lever Act of 1914, to a deep-rooted and accepted part of the educational program of rural America. The youth instruction, embodied in 4-H club work, was an important part of the planning in those days. At the very outset 4-H projects had been based quite largely on agriculture and home economics for country boys and girls with the feeling among the planners that most of them would remain on farms after they had completed their education.

In most cases the early projects related directly to subject matter departments within the colleges of agriculture, of which home economics was one, based almost exclusively on production and management practices.

With the new concept that 4-H club work can contribute to the needs and interests of all boys and girls, including those living in small towns, urban areas, and cities, projects needed to have wider boundaries. New projects were therefore designed to meet the needs and interests of an increasing number of boys and girls, many of whom did not live on rural routes.

The newer projects developed were also for farm boys and girls as well as small town and city youth, because they too needed more than production and management projects to maintain their interest. This streamlining of the program increased its popularity so that by 1930 more than 12,500 Missouri boys and girls were engaged in 4-H club work.

Junior Leadership was introduced in 1946 and was one of the early deviations from the older concept of projects. Even with 14 years of age being a prerequisite, the enrollment of 3,222 members in 105 counties in the state in 1961 proved the early acceptance of such a project.

It was developed within the state club staff, without any reference to a subject matter department of the College of Agriculture, or any other discipline of the University of Missouri. Charline Lindsay of the Missouri State 4-H Club Staff says:

"Junior Leadership from the very beginning appealed to the older teen members. It has made a substantial contribution to thousands of 4-H Club members, for it provides the arena in which youth perform in leadership roles for the first time. Missouri was the first state to publish Junior Leadership literature and one of the first to develop and hold Junior Leadership conferences in which young people are provided purposeful training in leadership skills. The entire club program has profited by the added dimension of leadership provided by the Junior Leaders".

Automotive care and safety was accepted as a project by the agricultural engineering department of the University of Missouri and was developed nationally for all boys and girls, not just rural members.

Photography as a project was introduced in the late 1950's, and it became increasingly popular as a tool in meeting the needs and interests of all 4-H club members, rural and urban alike.

Older projects were revised during this period to enlarge their scope. They were made of value to more boys and girls. When the "Working Dog for the Farm" project, introduced in 1952, was revised under the title "You and Your Dog" in 1960, it reached more members and became more popular.

Outdoorsman, a project with considerable flexibility and wide range of interest, was started in 1962. This project was planned especially to meet the interests of town and city youth. It was accepted equally well by the younger members in rural areas and especially in the small towns. It included an expanded leadership plan in that resource people were encouraged to handle the subject matter. This left the work of organization to the project leader.

Child care, after being thoroughly tested, was introduced into Missouri 4-H club work in 1962. This project also is especially designed to fit into the program of girls in urban areas and cities. It is used with equal success in rural areas.

In 1962, several new projects were introduced in selected counties on a pilot basis. These projects included small motors, general science, water safety, lawns, ham curing, rocks, pigeons, welding, library, guns, and grain marketing.

The project, because of emphasis on individual 4-H member development, still is the basis of 4-H work in Missouri. With the single exception of Junior Leadership, it can be said that every 4-H club project to the year 1960 was anchored in agriculture and home economics.

Projects based on practices approved by the Experiment Stations of the Land-Grant Colleges have been accepted criteria not only in Missouri but in other states as well. Standards have always been set in terms of requirements for a minimum amount of work acceptable for a completion. Demonstrating, exhibiting, judging (with a few exceptions), and recordkeeping have been considered an important part of project work.

A discussion of projects follows in alphabetical order, not necessarily in regard to their popularity with 4-H club members, or their importance in the entire Extension program.[24]

---

[24]Project information, as here presented, is from the Records of the Extension Service, University of Missouri, Columbia, Missouri.

Agricultural Economics

Agricultural economics plays a role in 4-H club work through farm management, the only 4-H project based strictly on the subject matter in this area. However, this department's services are in no way limited to projects attached to that department. Marketing cuts across many production projects. The tomato project in southeast Missouri is a good example. It carried the product through until the tomatoes were properly graded, packaged, and sold. Ted Joule's work as an Extension marketing specialist in poultry has been outstanding in egg and broiler marketing. Lamb shows and sales, 4-H feeder pig sales, and baby beef sales illustrate the part that marketing has played in standard 4-H projects. Buying and wearing of clothes could be classified at least partially as economics.

Agricultural Engineering

The first quarter century of 4-H work in Missouri passed before agricultural engineering 4-H projects were listed anywhere in its literature, with but one exception: that of a mention of a 4-H terracing project in 1930. The project apparently was not popular since there is no record of enrollment.

The expansion of 4-H project work in this area in the next 25 years is impressive and shows the following member participation in 1963:

Electricity (4 units)	2,690
Tractor maintenance (5 units)	1,150
Automotive (3 units)	1,049
Woodwork (6 units)	4,592
Farmstead improvement	66
Water management	35

The first agricultural engineering projects to be developed were in farm handicraft. Handicraft I was on ropework, Handicraft II was woodwork. The ropework project never progressed beyond the knot-tying stage. The woodwork project proved to be a very popular one.

Now that 4-H has spread to the cities and towns it has wide acceptance. In 1954, ropework as a project was dropped. Woodwork replaced what had formerly been called Handicraft II. This was developed into a six-unit project.

The 4-H electricity project members include small boys making a "pig-tail" splice, to older ones engaged in wiring a house, and in some cases serving as electrician's apprentices. Starting in 1946, the program has grown to four projects with an enrollment of 2,690 in 1963. The 4-H Electric Theater, air conditioned, in the Missouri State Fair Building at Sedalia was readied for use in 1959. Approximately 2,000 visited the theater and sat through one, or more, demonstrations during the State Fair in 1960, the second year of operation.

The first state-wide effort to develop the electricity project through leader training came in 1953. Agricultural engineering specialists, power company men, and many REA technicians and administrators have contributed to the development of this project.

The tractor maintenance project was developed in 1944. The first school for training tractor project leaders was held in December, 1944. The tractor sessions have varied from one-day sessions to four-day sessions but have always been held annually. These training sessions have been sponsored for many years by the Standard Oil Company of Indiana. The Skilled Operator's Contest soon became a part of county programs. The first State Skilled Operator's Contest was held at the Missouri State Fair in 1953.

The automotive project, limited to members 15 years of age or over, was started on a pilot basis in 1957. St. Louis, Boone, Lafayette, Scotland and Newton counties were the original pilot counties. The project was offered statewide in 1959, three units were developed and the enrollment reached 4,378 in 1963. The Firestone Tire and Rubber Company sponsors the program.

Farmstead improvement was confined for many years to metal roofing work under sponsorship. Many field demonstrations were held, and much good was done in the preservation of metal roofs. However, when the awards program was discontinued the enrollment declined. The present farmstead improvement project is very different from the program that originally was titled farmstead improvement. Started in 1956, it consists of such things as farmstead arrangement, cattle guards, and some buildings. It is a comprehensive program often covering several years. A high enrollment was never anticipated. Members are left largely to their own initiative.

The water management project is another "grown man's" undertaking that starts with a complete water management plan for a farm and takes several years for completion of the program.

Beef

The beef project has grown from a one calf project in 1918 with 508 club members participating, to five projects in 1963 with enrollments as follows:

Baby beef	2,591
Young cattlemen	69
Breeding heifer	587
Cow & calf	735
Beef herd	386
TOTAL	4,368

Shows, fairs and expositions have played an important part in beef projects. The American Royal Livestock Show at Kansas City has had 4-H baby beef classes since 1922. The county group of "five steers class" was first offered in 1928, and changed a little 4-H Baby Beef State Fair show to a big show. Classes have often exceeded 50 entries. In 1956, steer classes were divided on a weight basis. In recent years steer entries have leveled off, but breeding classes have made a consistent gain. Often the baby beef program has been "exploited", but despite this situation, much good has resulted from it, and often members have gone on to become young cattlemen, and later in life outstanding commercial or purebred breeders.

Critics of the 4-H club baby beef project have claimed that it is an impractical project. Some have intimated that former 4-H members now feeding cattle as a business never follow the 4-H finishing pattern. Some believe that the show encourages professionalism.

There are cases on record where a boy has paid an exceptionally high price for a calf and gambled on hitting the "jackpot" with a grand champion that might bring a fabulous sale price. There are exceptions, but generally county agents and 4-H leaders have consistently encouraged keeping the feeding operations on a practical basis but have not discouraged striving for a high finish.

Prime beef has not been considered an unworthy goal. Good operators have generally shown a profit over cost of animal and feed. Most of those who have gambled have paid a high price for their folly.

Few Missouri 4-H boys and girls have been misled by the "pot of gold at the end of the rainbow." And certainly the Producer Sale at East St. Louis and the young cattleman's project both are on a practical basis.

The boy and his baby beef has done more to acquaint the public with 4-H club work than any other project. More men have been attracted to 4-H leadership by the baby beef program than any other meat animal project.

Many of the baby beef members have purchased breeding stock with their profits and started herds of their own. A herd of beef cattle developed from a single 4-H heifer is considered the highest achievement in 4-H beef project work.

Citizenship

Should one condense the 4-H objective to an all-inclusive one, it would read like this: "To encourage the development of good citizenship." Yet Missouri has no 4-H citizenship project or activity. One might ask, "What part does citizenship play in the 4-H program?" The answer would be that citizenship training started when club work started. It is woven into every fiber of the 4-H program.

The act of accepting the responsibilities of a voluntary organization requiring purposes, self-reliance, and persistence is a first step. Following through with daily efforts, achieving, and sharing take a 4-H member up the rungs of the citizenship ladder.

Patriotism, too, must not be overlooked. Membership participation in acts and events patriotic in nature, include the following:

1. Pledge of Allegiance.
2. Display of Old Glory
3. Good government days.
4. Annual citizenship ceremonies for 20-year-old members at State 4-H Club Week.
5. Electing officers and district representatives at State Club Week following the pattern of county elections.
6. Guided tours of county courthouses, State Capitol, and National Capitol.

7. Visits of National 4-H Conference and National Citizenship Short course delegations to national shrines and with Presidents and Congressmen.

8. Participation in Citizenship National Awards Programs.

9. Participation in National 4-H Citizenship Short Courses at the National 4-H Center in Washington, D. C.

Clothing

4-H clothing work was first designated as "Sewing", then as "Garment Making" and finally "Clothing." Starting with a single project in 1914, the second and third years were added in 1923, and IV, V, and VI by 1940. "Buying and Wearing Clothes" was added in 1958, and "Knitting" in 1962. The growth in enrollment has been consistent, reaching five figures in the 1940's and stabilizing around 12,000 in the sixties.

The dress revue was originated for club use in the early 1920's. The first state dress revue was held at the State Fair in 1925. Lorene Hostetter of Jackson County was the first State Dress Revue winner. The revue has retained its popularity at all levels: club, county, district, state, and nation. It is safe to say that most of the girls who have advanced beyond the third year of clothing work have been evaluated in a dress revue at some time. Many have started by modeling aprons very early and at the county level. Many are now designing and making their own trousseau.

Local leaders have encouraged members to go beyond meeting their own clothing needs and assist in meeting the needs of others, especially younger members of their families. The trend in this direction is pronounced in the individual reports of long time clothing project members.

Demonstrating, judging, and exhibiting have been a part of the program almost from the very beginning.

There have been no "snap course" clothing projects. They have been challenging all the way. The dress revue has served as a stimulus to this project since early days in Extension.

Crops

In 1915, there were 1,178 boys enrolled in corn production projects who reported to the State 4-H Club Office as club members. Forty-five years later, 1960, there were 1,191 enrolled in crops. During this 45-year period, the total number decreased to 72 in 1933 and reached a peak of 1,762 in 1953. Only 13 of these years produced enrollments in excess of 1,000 members.

Early projects centered around corn, pigs, and canning. Interest in corn production had an influence on the passage of the Smith-Lever Act in 1914, the Act that brought Extension work into existence. Many boys were growing corn for shows and yield contests prior to the start of Extension work.

In 1960, some 673 club projects (well over half the total crops projects) were corn. In fact, corn has held the majority of field crop projects all through the years. A "hundred bushels to the acre" goal was set by many 4-H groups enrolled in corn production in the post-war years. This challenge stimulated many to achieve this goal.

Soybeans became acceptable as a 4-H project as early as 1923. It has continued to have a modest enrollment, 162 members in 1960.

Since World War II, cotton production has had some attraction for 4-H members in southeast Missouri cotton producing counties. Many groups set a goal of two bales to the acre. Some 113 members were enrolled in the cotton project in 1960. Tobacco has been recognized as a worthy project, but enrollment has always been light.

Requests for project material on other cereal grains, legumes, and grasses brought about the organization of a project that would include these crops. A legumes and grasses project was offered for the first time in 1956. The material provided for acreage minimums, variety, rate of seeding, time of seeding, and fertilization recommendations. No leaders are specifically trained for it. Less than 100 have enrolled in it annually. Yet from this limited number have come very often Missouri's Crop Congress winners and delegates to the Board of Trade Conference in Chicago.

Crops projects have lent themselves in excellent manner to public demonstrations. Many of the things that were demonstrated during the early years such as seed corn selection, rag doll tester, and the like have gone out as hybrid corn came in.

Hybrid corn tended to decrease interest in grain judging and grain exhibiting since the major exhibit in crops had always been 10 ears of corn. Since 1940, the show and training in judging have played a minor role in the crops project program.

Dairy

The Boys and Girls Annual Report which first mentioned dairy project enrollment was made in 1919, and it showed 179 members.

The dairy project as a part of club work actually had its beginning in what were called calf clubs as early as 1917.

The qualifications for calf club membership were not well defined at that time. The adults interested in dairy clubs seemed more interested in breed promotion. Most of the project animals involved were calves. There were no requirements, no literature, and no records.

A. C. Ragsdale, University of Missouri dairy specialist in 1918, said: "The calf club movement has been so general that it has swept everything before it, resulting in approximately 90 so-called calf clubs being organized and in the purchase of 3,600 dairy calves and heifers. This has been much abused in that boys and girls were lost sight of in the effort to simply get more cows, and little attention was given to supplying instructions in care and feeding. The heifers were sold after a short period of ownership—a practice which brands one as a 'cow dealer' rather than a breeder. Out of all this, however, has grown a plan which is fundamentally correct."

Dairy expanded to three projects in 1922: Dairy Calf I, Dairy Heifer II, and later, Dairy Cow III. A cow testing project was started in 1927. It was short-lived.

Dairy herd was designated as a project in 1953. Two or more producing cows qualified as a herd. Ten years later, in 1963, enrollments were:

Dairy calf I	481
Dairy heifer II	572
Dairy cow III	285
Dairy herd	242
TOTAL	1,580

Enrollments in 1950, 1951, and 1953 all exceeded 3,000. A peak of 3,177 was reached in 1950.

Marion County had the first and most successful purebred club in 1918. Thirty-three bred heifers were purchased at a cost of $3,200. These were sold with their offspring for $10,780.

Sixty-four purebred Guernsey heifers were imported from the Island of Guernsey in 1919 for members of Egypt Mills in Cape Girardeau County. S. M. Carter was responsible for this project.

The Barnett Heifer Club in Morgan County in 1920 produced 27 calves from ARO dams and was considered by the Extension dairy specialists at the time as "ideal calf club work."

C. M. Long, Pettis County agent, did successful club work with grade heifers in the early 1920's.

Greene, St. Francois, Cole, Morgan, St. Charles, Callaway, and Lincoln Counties carried on outstanding dairy project work in 1921.

Entomology

There are at least four reasons why Missouri has recognized entomology as a project area: 1. Missouri has a Department of Entomology in the College of Agriculture. 2. Boys like to chase butterflies. 3. There needs to be a place for apiary culture. 4. It is important economically.

A bee project was introduced into the 4-H program early. It is a sound project. Membership has never reached 100, but it will doubtless be continued indefinitely.

An insect study project was developed in the 1930's along with other low-investment projects. It has educational value and was quite popular in the 1940's. During the period when it flourished, some splendid collections and mountings were made.

Insect study is one of the discontinued projects. After this project was dropped in the 1950's, there continued to be some demand from 4-H members for an insect project. In 1957, the project was revised and organized into a four-year series that made a place for collections, but required some controls in the first three years. The fourth year project in this area is known as Entomology IV, Bees.

Foods

From 1955 to 1963, inclusive, foods projects enrollment has exceeded all others in numbers. In 1963, some 14,125 were enrolled in foods projects. Clothing was second in number with 12,920 members. All meat animal projects totaled that year 7,289. In fact, the food enrollment exceeded meat animal, dairy, and poultry combined. Not only has this project grown to be the largest in number, it was the first popular project for girls.

In 1914, the first year of club work, there were 278 members enrolled in foods projects. Some 180 of these were canning projects. The work was limited to cold-pack canning of tomatoes. Baking projects were soon added to the program. Then a school lunch project was added. These were projects within the school in which almost all leaders were teachers and the number enrolled far exceeded that of all other food projects.

Many clothing projects were conducted in the schools. Canning, being a seasonal thing, became an important summer project. During the 1920's and far into the 1930's, it was not uncommon for home demonstration agents to give less time to home economics clubs during the summer and concentrate on 4-H clubs. During this period, some of the best home economics demonstration teams were developed.

By 1930, the hot lunch clubs had diminished to 15 in the state with a membership of 122, and soon they ended completely. At that time, projects were developed in food preparation and food preservation. These two areas were gradually developed until they were six food preparation projects and four food preservation projects.

Nationally sponsored programs were developed for dairy foods, and later, frozen foods, under the leadership of what was then the National Committee on Boys and Girls Culb Work. One of these fell into the food preparation area and the other in food preservation, but specific projects were never developed for either of them. In 1956 the home economics Extension staff and the 4-H staff decided to study carefully the food and nutrition 4-H project program. A representative of the Federal Extension Service, Missouri food and nutrition specialists, members of the 4-H club staff, and five home agents served on a committee to revise the food project plan. This resulted in the development of eight food projects in which food preparation and preservation were combined.

Home agents had a great deal to do with planning subject matter for the first two years of food work. Foods I circulars were written and mimeographed. More attention was given to the needs and interests of the differnent ages. The first five projects were designed for the 10 to 15-year-old members. Project literature was written to appeal to boys as well as girls. Foods VI to VIII were designed for older girls and boys and included "buymanship."

Demonstrations have been important in foods projects. Subject matter lends itself to a presentation by the demonstration method. Both foods preservation judging and food preparation judging have been included in achievement day programs beginning with the county achievement program and continuing through district and state achievement events. Exhibits have played an important role in the foods program from the earliest days.

It is worthy of note that foods projects have not suffered in popularity with the coming of the community-type 4-H club organization. The total enrollment of foods projects in 1937 was 4,215. Enrollment exceeded 10,000 for the first time in 1954.

There has been no effort to single out a foods girl annually as is done in the dress revue for clothing. However, a "State Home Economics Girl" has been selected for many years. Foods have consistently had a prominent place in the overall records of girls interested in home economics.

Forestry

Forestry was offered in 4-H work for the first time in 1935. Forestry appreciation was the title of the first circular in this area. The work phase consisted of collections of wood, leaves, and fruit, all properly labeled.

One project, forest seeding, is intended to stimulate the production of seedlings for farm plantings. The development of forestry nurseries by the Missouri Department of Conservation provided a source of seedlings at a nominal cost, so the nursery phase of this work did not develop significantly.

Forestry had a prominent place in the 4-H camp program especially in the state conservation camps started in 1936 and continued each year until 1958. It was followed by wildlife conservation workshops at State Club Week. The commercial aspect of this combined project and activity effort was limited to the production of Christmas trees. This provided for a substantial source of income in many southern counties.

Forestry appreciation had its highest acceptance in the thirties when non-investment projects were popular. In 1938 some 3,433 club projects were carried out. During World War II there was a decline in 4-H forestry but enrollments still ranged from 200 to 400.

The 4-H forestry literature was revised in 1953. It provided for three projects: Forestry Appreciation I; Forestry Seedling II; and Planting and Woodland Management III.

Home Grounds

The home grounds project was introduced in 1935. By the 1940's more than 1,000 were enrolled, more than 2,000 by the 1950's. A complete revision and expansion into six projects occurred in the 1960's. Subject matter ranges from growing flowers and arranging bouquets to landscaping the homestead.

Home Management

Young housekeeper projects were offered as early as 1922. There was an enrollment of seventeen. Then came Young Homemakers and later Home Furnishings, More Attractive Homes, and during the World War II years a Home Service project was introduced.

Home Furnishings I and II were the mainstays in this area for a number of years. In 1956, the 4-H homemaking series was completely revised by a committee from Federal, State and County Extension Services, resulting in a comprehensive series of seven units. A listing of the projects in this series by title indicates program content:

"Brighten a Spot"
"Create a Pleasant Place to Eat"
"Arrange a Place to Sleep"
"Organize a Place for Everything"
"Provide a Place to Work or Play"
"Fashion a Grooming Corner"
"Decorate a Complete Room"

Leaflets containing printed subject matter are provided. Many references are given. An effort is made to adapt the project to the situation in which the individual member finds himself or herself, and is designed with the idea of appealing to boys as well as to girls.

Horse and Horsemanship

The first 4-H colt club was started in 1930 with five members. After a lapse of three years, 36 members were enrolled in 1934, and 97 in 1935. A 4-H circular on growing and care for colts was published in 1936.

Horse and mule colts were shown at halter, and ownership by the club member was a requirement. Some worthy colt classes were shown at the State Fair in the late 1930's and early 1940's.

Interest in this project decreased until a horsemanship project was offered in 1950. An excellent circular in this area was published in 1952. Growth in the project has been gradual, and it is now a popular project. In 1963 some 2,524 members were enrolled. Ownership is not a requirement but most mounts are individually owned by the members including ponies, quarter horses, saddle horses, parade horses, and some ordinary "nags."

Four-H horsemanship classes have not been offered at the Missouri State Fair, but such classes have been popular at local shows. Experienced horsemen and women have furnished most of the leadership for 4-H project groups.

Horticulture

Gardening projects began in 1917, at the beginning of World War I. Enrollment reached the all-time high of 10,289 in 1919. Then horticulture as a club project declined and remained in three figures until 1941. World War II influence was felt. The enrollment in 1941 was 664, and in 1942 it was 6,615. It has ranged downward until the enrollments remained between 3,000 and 4,000 during the 1950's.

In addition to the home garden, there have been special projects in tomatoes, potatoes, sweet potatoes, peanuts, melons, sweet corn, and some other single crop projects. Projects have recognized production for home use and for market. Most of the single crop projects have been for market.

A project has been offered in "strawberries" and one in "small fruits" for several years. The enrollment at times has been substantial in the strawberry project. Small fruits have never been very popular as a project. In 1960 there were only seven enrolled in small fruits and two in strawberries.

During the forties and early part of the fifties, garden projects were designated as Vegetable I, II, and III. Vegetable I was a single crop project for family use. Vegetable II was production for market. Vegetable III involved the home garden. Organization of the project changed in the middle 1950's to a series of three based on a challenge. The first and the most elemental of these is called "Watch Your Garden Grow Up" and involves production of root, leaf, and fruit vegetables.

Number II, "Growing and Marketing" gets into the money-making phase. Number III, "Growing Vegetables for Family, Food and Fun" is the home garden project. In 1960, about 70 percent of horticulture enrollment was in Vegetable I and 25 percent in Vegetable II.

Competitive vegetable judging introduced in the early 1940's has proved to be quite popular. Vegetable judging has both a production and consumer aspect. Moreover, it lends itself to teaching the techniques of judging because of the wide range of possibilities in setting up classes.

A comprehensive program was developed with Negro 4-H members in the late 1940's. This had some Sears-Roebuck Foundation sponsorship. It was a tomato project that started with the selection of approved, disease resistant varieties and carried through to the marketing of wrapped tomatoes. It required effective spraying, fertilization, grading, and packaging. It was one of the best and most complete of the educational programs ever conducted in the state.

Junior Leadership

Junior Leadership does not follow the criteria for a production project. First established as a project in 1945, it marks the breaking away place from strictly agriculture and home economics projects. While some junior leaders assume adult leader responsibilities, the objective was, and is to develop well-rounded leadership.

The project involves planning, setting goals, and implementing action that leads to achievement of goals. It is a "purpose, plan, and push" project. Emphasis is given to presiding, chairing committees, serving on committees, public speaking, demonstrating, news writing, radio and television programs, assisting adult leaders, assisting younger members, recruiting members, hosting, implementing National Short Course Citizenship participation, State Council work, and similar activities.

Four-H work has contributed to the development of 4-H member leaders from its beginning. Leaders naturally grew out of purposefulness and participation in club work. The conscious effort to develop 4-H leadership as one of the major objectives for upper teenagers started in 1948. Fifty-four were enrolled the first year. The enrollment has grown to approximately 25 percent of those of eligible age.

Many things have contributed to the development of the junior leadership project.

Junior leader camp conferences were held annually during the four-year period of 1954-1957. In 1957, some 145 junior leaders attended, representing 74 counties. State membership doubled and tripled during that time.

District junior leader camp conferences were started in 1956 and have been continued, with three to six conferences in number and with 390 persons participating in the earlier years and from 500 to 600 in later years.

Eleven state 4-H health camp conferences and two conferences for chairmen of health committees have been held.

Many state wildlife conservation conferences were devoted almost exclusively to junior leaders. Members of conservation standing committees were given preference in the selection of delegates.

Public speaking for junior leaders was made a part of county, district, and state achievement programs in 1954. Since 1956, Southwestern Bell Telephone Company has sponsored this program and has given awards to district and state winners.

Missouri participation in the National Citizenship Short Course has been the largest of any state. All Missouri delegates are junior leaders. Thirty-one participated in 1960; 219 in 1961; 301 in 1962; 310 in 1963; and 388 in 1964.

Virtually all Club Week delegates in recent years have been junior leaders.

Poultry

In 1930 Earl and Stanley Rader of Blue Ridge, Jackson County, had a 300-baby chick project and carried the framework for a 10' by 12' brooder house across the state to compete in the poultry section of the National Dairy Show at St. Louis.

A basic project through the years has been one in which the members started with eggs or baby chicks and brought the pullets into production in the fall for the first year and continued with a flock project in succeeding years. During World War II, a device was introduced that stimulated this basic project.

The device was a combination brooder and shelter in which a member might take 50 to 75 baby chicks, brood them in an oil brooder, move them into the shelter that later became a laying house for the limited number of pullets that could be brooded under these conditions. This unit was economical and one that could be constructed by a member old enough to use a saw and hammer. Members in Carter County, among others, constructed many of these brooders.

In the mid-fifties, Ted Joule, University of Missouri poultry marketing specialist, did some splendid work in training junior leaders in a consumer education program with quality eggs. Poultry project members consistently participated in the State 4-H Poultry Judging Contest. Every state team that had an opportunity participated in interstate contests.

One of the interesting projects in recent years was the "Chicken of Tomorrow" Contest. This was a good title for a broiler project. It had good hatchery support.

Extension poultry project specialists have directed the State Fair show program, the second day of which always concluded with a dressed bird auction. Dressed birds made a feature 4-H exhibit at the Missouri State Fair.

Missouri has been represented at the Junior Poultry Fact Finding Conference by four outstanding poultry project members every year since the conference started in 1954.

In recent years, bantams and pigeons are attracting some attention. These projects are finding favor in some suburban communities.

Science

In 1961, the areas of interest of 4-H club members included science projects. This is a departure from the established pattern. It is based on the "why" rather than the "how to do." It opened up a whole new field of adventure, study, resourcefulness, and challenge to the inquiring mind.

The National 4-H Foundation originally authorized a special study of the possibilities of expanding the understanding and use of science through 4-H club work.

Early areas of interest included climatology, animal science, textiles, plant science, and electronics. The first start in this direction in Missouri was in the field of animal science.

Sheep

Sheep husbandry is a natural for both boys and girls. Most of the projects make use of grade ewes and registered rams. Five ewes have been the minimum number for project use. The time involved is breeding time to marketing of wool and lamb crop. An 80-pound spring lamb in 100 days has been an accepted project goal.

The first sheep project was started in 1918, when club boys and girls in six counties had 82 members. Saline County had 65, Lafayette 6, Cape Girardeau 6, Pettis 3, and one each in Grundy and Macon Counties.

The best example of 4-H project promotion and successful operation is the Missouri Western Ewe Promotion.

In a project in which there is low apparent interest, the procedure with both Extension workers and 4-H club leaders is to inform prospective members of requirements, instruct them on fundamentals, and then leave them largely to their own as to timing, procurement, practices and marketing.

This procudure may, or may not, bring a high percentage of successful projects—ones that bring pride and satisfaction. The matter rests primarily with initiative of members and advice of their fathers.

Compare that way of doing things with the following procedure that was used from the start in the Missouri Western Ewe Promotion:

1. Animal husbandry Extension specialist arranges with the Producers Livestock Marketing Association to contract for ewes in carlot or double-deck lots in July.

2. County agents meet with prospective ewe and lamb project members and their dads, in the summer, to discuss details of the overall plan, practices to follow, approximate cost of ewes, securing of rams, plans for deliveries, breeding, dipping, pasturing, distribution, financing, and insuring of ewes.

3. Project leader meets with project group and supervises feeding, management, and "follow-through" on plans.

4. Hold County Lamb Show in June, with lambs going to market the following day.

5. Sell wool on a graded basis.

Plans don't always work out, but the percentage of successful sheep projects has been very high.

This carlot movement of breeding ewes for 4-H ewe and lamb project members began in 1936. Then a carlot of ewes was distributed to 71 members in Randolph County under the leadership of W. M. Woods, county agent. Audrain County followed in 1937. In 1940 some 2,175 solid-mouth ewes were distributed to 4-H members in seven northeast Missouri counties. These were big, strong ewes and were delivered to members in November, bred and insured for $7 per head.

In 1944 some 8,216 Texas yearlings were distributed in 27 counties and 5,000 Montana yearlings in 1942. A total of 41 counties participated in this ewe program. E. S. Matteson, Extension livestock specialist, in cooperation with county agents and 4-H club staff members, established the pattern. It continued for many years.

The pattern included: (1) Arrange for financing at a local bank; (2) ship ewes in August; (3) buy registered Hampshire rams at state Extension supervised breeder ram sales; (4) arrange for pasture for county purchase for breeding; (5) dip for tick control; (6) distribute insured ewes in November; (7) market rams late in season, charging difference between the purchase price and sale price against the project; and (8) hold show and sale in June.

By 1938 the sheep project enrollment reached "four figures" with 1,225 members participating. The number increased normally to 2,273 in 1942 then gradually declined to one thousand figures in 1950's.

Soil Conservation

Two soil conservation projects were developed in the early 1930's. The 4-H circulars entitled "Know Your Soil" and "Know Your Farm" were published in 1935. The projects had limited acceptance.

These, however, were the only 4-H projects that bore a soil name until a soil fertility project was developed and introduced on a pilot basis in 1958 in Shelby, Benton, Polk, Laclede, Pettis, and Saline Counties. It is one of the most advanced projects ever offered to 4-H members in that it is a three-year project involving a three-year rotation.

Swine

Pig clubs are almost as old as 4-H work. The first ones were organized in 1916. There were 31 clubs that year in 13 counties. The enrollment was 271 members. They were called pig feeding projects and were projects in which members fed a single pig to market weight. Some 15 members were credited with having completed this project that first year of 1916.

In 1963 swine project enrollment showed the following: purebred gilt, 287; market pig, 510; sow and litter, 1,567, for a total of 2,364.

Peak enrollment for this project was 4,221 in 1951. Two-thirds of the enrollment in swine projects has been in the most challenging of the three, the sow and litter project.

Numerous instances may be cited to show that 4-H played a prominent role in the improvement of breeding stock in the early Extension years. In 1918, some 60 members organized a purebred gilt club of Durocs and spotted Poland Chinas in Caldwell County. In December, 1921, some 133 bred gilts (Duroc, Spotted Poland China, and Poland China) were distributed to boys and girls in bred gilt clubs in Pettis County. In 1920, Linn County had 41 members in bred gilt clubs.

During the next quarter century, good breeding stock became generally distributed. There was still a need for upgrading breeding stock for the commercial producer. Emphasis shifted to breeding and crossbreeding of meat-type hogs.

This is best shown by a program for improving the quality of feeder pigs in the south central area of Missouri. Beginning in October, 1945, 25 choice meat-type Hampshire gilts and 10 boars carefully selected by E. S. Matteson, Extension specialist, were distributed in Dent, Oregon, Howell, Ripley, and Shannon Counties.

The Sears-Roebuck Foundation sponsored this project. The five gilts allotted to a county provided the project animals for a single project group. Ten weanling gilts given by project members in payment for the bred gilts they received provided gilts for starting a new project group within the county and a second project group in another county.

This program in time was extended to 10 counties in south central Missouri in what is known as the "feeder pig area" of the state. It gave stimulus to an extensive feeder pig sale program for 4-H members and adults in this area. Feeder pig sales soon became very popular, patterned after the feeder calf sales, in the period following World War II. Consignments from 4-H members were notable in many of the sales, often open to adults and youth alike.

Vienna, county seat of Maries County, claims credit for being the place where the first strictly 4-H feeder pig sale in the United States was held. This came about as a result of voluntary effort by boys and their dads from eight counties in the Vienna area. Nine counties were finally involved in this effort. No outside sponsorship was involved. Ste. Genevieve County later developed a 4-H feeder pig sale. And so the movement spread.

Pig chains sponsored by Sears-Roebuck Foundation date back to the 1930's. Actually hundreds of registered gilts were distributed to 4-H members with the payback of a gilt or two gilts to other members.

* * *

A breeding program which included 10 counties in the Kansas City area was started under the Sears-Roebuck Foundation sponsorship in 1950. Shows and sales of breeding stock (Hampshire and Duroc) spread good breeding stock in this area for 10 years or more.

New Madrid County has featured a fat barrow show annually since 1946. The peak number consigned in this show was 153 in 1959.

Breeding stock shows have played a minor role in 4-H pork production. The 4-H swine exhibits at the Missouri State Fair attracted some attention back in the middle 1930's when Raymond Kahrs and Raymond Klein of Smithton exhibited purebred pigs. The sons of Raymond Kahrs have been seen often in 4-H and FFA Poland China show rings for many years.

Since World War II the quality of 4-H swine exhibits at the State Fair has been of much higher quality than in the 1930's.

Some enthusiasm was developed for a state barrow show and sale in the late 1940's. One of the best 4-H exhibits of swine at the State Fair of all time was that of Dee C. Hunter, a twelve-year-old 4-H member from Knobnoster in Johnson County. His Berkshire litter of 12 pigs swept all the honors at the State Fair Junior Show and won high honors at the National Barrow Show in Austin, Minnesota that year. Hunter was the youngest exhibitor at the event and his litter was proclaimed the world's record litter. Dee's father was a 4-H member in the early 1920's. (See Chapter VI for more on the St. Joseph show.)

4-H Club Projects and Relationship
to College Departments

During the 50-year period between 1914 and 1964, there have been 15 subject matter departments or schools in the University of Missouri College of Agriculture. Most of the 4-H projects have had a definite tie-in with subject matter departments and schools. Extension specialists have prepared most of the 4-H literature and the content has had approval of department chairmen. A summary of the 4-H project relationship is given here.

Animal Husbandry Department

Beef	- 5 projects
Swine	- 3 projects
Sheep	- 2 projects
Horse	- 1 projects

Dairy Department

Dairy	- 4 projects

Poultry Department

Poultry	- 3 projects

Horticulture Department

Vegetable	- 3 projects

Small fruits, special crops like potato, tomato and melons are now discontinued.

Field Crops Department

Corn	- 1 project
Soybeans	- 1 project
Cotton	- 1 project
Small grain, Legumes, and Grasses	- 1 project

A grain sorghum project has been discontinued.

Soils Department

Soil Fertility	- 1 project

Agricultural Engineering Department

Automotive	- 3 projects
Electricity	- 4 projects
Farmstead Improvement	- 1 project
Small Engines	- 1 project
Tractor Management	- 4 projects
Woodwork	- 6 projects
Water Management	- 2 projects

Entomology Department

Entomology	- 3 projects
Bees	- 1 project

Agricultural Economics Department

Farm Management	- 1 project

School of Forestry

Forestry	- 3 projects

School of Home Economics

Clothing	- 7 projects
Knitting	- 4 projects
Food & Nutrition	- 8 projects
Home Management	- 7 projects
Child Care	- 2 projects

School of Veterinary Medicine

Dog	- 1 project

There is no direct relation to project work in Departments of Agricultural Chemistry or Rural Sociology. The Department of Extension Education has no 4-H projects as such but is very much involved in 4-H Leadership and program activities.

The 4-H staff assumes full responsibility for other projects, most of which have been recently added to Manual 50, which carries the official list of projects. To the contents of that manual the following should now be added:

Junior Leadership
> The Speech Department and staff members of the University of Missouri School of Journalism assume some responsibilities in this program.

Outdoorsman - 20 Project Units
> The major subject matter source is the Missouri Department of Conservation.

Photography - 3 Units

Career Exploration - 1 Project
> The Counselling Service in the Extension Division of Administration of the University, the Department of Education and others contributed to the development of this project.

Rabbits - 1 Project

Swimming and Rescue - 1 Project
> Individual members of the state club staff are the subject matter source for this project.

4-H Activities

The purpose of 4-H activities as stated in the Missouri Projects and Activities Manual, published in 1960, is to provide opportunities in knowledge, cooperation, consideration for others, social adjustment, and leadership. The activities that are catalogued are: courtesies, community improvement, first aid, grooming, health, marketing, recreation, safety, and wildlife conservation.

The word "activity" has a very wide application. Some consider demonstrating, judging, and exhibiting to be 4-H activities. Some say camping is a 4-H activity. Missouri has attempted to place limitations on the broad meaning of the word by placing "4-H" in front of it in literature and programs.

Consistency therefore decreed that a formula be developed for both the project and the activity. With the coming of the community-type 4-H club, the 4-H activity became a very important part of the whole program. The transition from the project-type to the community-type club covered a 10-year period, beginning in 1938. During this period some planning along this line was done with the following results:

Projects	Activities
Restricted Primarily to Agriculture and Home Economics	Based on areas of interest of all young people
Subject matter source - Land–Grant College	Subject matter source - Land-Grant College and other sources
Selected by individual	Selected by club
Requirements	No requirements
Records	Records optional
Adult leaders	Motivated by standing committee of members with an adult advisor

Four-H club "activities" began in the 1920's. "Everyday courtesies" was the first activity introduced by the state club staff at that time. While it was not given status with a printed circular until 1936, certain materials were supplied that helped project clubs to include "etiquette" in their programs. Incidentally, the *activity* now called simply "courtesies" is still active. It has enjoyed outstanding popularity among 4-H members for many years.

Wildlife conservation was next introduced as an activity. Some loose-leaf material was made available to club members by the Missouri Department of Conservation. It was given status at the first annual State Conservation Camp in 1932. Wildlife conservation had a prominent place in county 4-H camping programs from their start. A printed 4-H circular on wildlife conservation was published in 1950.

Other printed circulars appeared in this order: Posture 1939, grooming 1940, music appreciation 1942, safety 1947, marketing 1955. Community service or community improvement gained some degree of popularity during the fifties. These were considered as "elective activities."

Every community-type club was expected to select an activity and carry it out as part of its program for a year or for several years. Selecting activities for the coming year became one of the items of business at the annual club meeting in October.

Health and first-aid were introduced into the 4-H program of Missouri as projects. They were popular in clubs formed in schools, and they continued to enjoy an enrollment in the thousands for a number of years. They were officially dropped as projects in 1941. Since then, Health has been regarded as an activity, and as health is one of the corner stones of 4-H, every club is expected to include a health activity in its program.

Health standing committees developed sufficient momentum so that two state-wide workshops and several health camp conferences were held for health committee chairmen. Splendid results have followed. Many junior leaders have exercised their leadership in health programs.

A health yardstick was introduced in 1942. This was a device for assisting club members in making a check of their health habits at the beginning of the club year and in evaluating it at the end of the year. A printed circular was published in 1952.

Music appreciation merited a publication as an activity in 1941. However, it was replaced by "singing" which became a part of the general recreational program. For many years "recreation" was included but not classified as either an activity or a project. The first recreation circular was published in 1932 and revised in 1946. Recreation is now usually regarded as another activity in which all clubs take part.

The 1940's were the formative years for activity programs. The real start along this line came in 1949. That year the first camp conference for community leaders was held, and a large part of the program was devoted to activities. One camp conference that year grew to six or more in following years. In these sessions, program planning has been a part of the community leader training program in which activities have been stressed.

Voluntary leaders early accepted the idea that community meetings should be of interest to all members. Project subject matter, demonstrating, judging, exhibit training, and recordkeeping were included in project meetings under the direction of leaders, and separated from regular monthly community meetings.

Junior project chairmen reports were made a part of the regular order of business of the community club meeting. Project demonstrations were given by members of the respective projects. But since activities were of the club's own selection, it was assumed that a great deal of the program would be built around these activities.

Many of the older clubs set up five standing committees: Program, membership, health, recreation, and selected activity. The program committee has the responsibility of planning and carrying out programs at the monthly club meetings.

Three activities—health, recreation, and a choice of wildlife conservation, safety, grooming or courtesies—served as themes for the day in the first series of leaders' meetings in 1950. The meetings involved nearly every county in the state. Many counties have continued to hold leader meetings of this type annually with leaders as guests at luncheons.

State Wildlife Conservation Camp Conferences, State Health Conferences, State Junior Leader Conferences, two State Health Workshops, Club Week Workshops, and many district Junior Leader Camp Confereces have stressed activity programs.

The entire junior leader program has contributed to the development of activities. Much of the junior leadership program has been done through standing committees. Health camp conference programs were designed for junior leaders who were chairmen or members of health committees in their home clubs. Conservationcamp delegates were selected in a similar way.

Many junior leaders who attended state and district junior leader camp conferences have been selected because of their achievements in the activity field. Many topics in the junior leader public speaking programs have had activities as subject matter. For several years, State Club Week Workshops have been built around activities.

The part activities play in the whole 4-H club program cannot be stressed too strongly. Their importance to a well-rounded program of 4-H has long been known by the state and local leaders.

Methods

"Demonstrations, judging, and exhibits have been an important part of Boys' and Girls' Club work from the very beginning, both as teaching methods and as contest features," says Jane Hinote, who has devoted almost a lifetime to 4-H club work. She says that standard club requirements were first used in 1918, when each club had to give a demonstration, have a judging team, and have an exhibit to complete its project work.

Demonstrations telling and showing what a member is doing are for the purpose of presenting information to others. Demonstrations, based on project work, have been used competitively to encourage boys and girls to improve quality of their work.

In the early years of club work in Missouri, three members constituted a team, and each was supposed to be busy every second. The earliest demonstration teams competed on a state-wide basis in 1919, with these results:

Dunklin County, 1st;
Scott County (Oran Team), 2nd;
Cape Girardeau County, 3rd.

The following year Butler County won the top award with Mrs. H. O. Harrawood as leader of the club.

Team demonstration contests and exhibits were also held at the Missouri State Fair at Sedalia; there are no records of winners until 1920. The 1920 Annual Report for Boys' and Girls' Club work states: "Seven demonstration teams entered the contest at the State Fair."

A new feature for Missouri in 1920 was the training of garment-making demonstration teams. That year two such teams demonstrated at the State Fair. One composed of Edith Patterson, Fay Hicks, and Christina Hicks from the Gulf Club of Greene County won first place honors and the trip to the Interstate Fair at Sioux City, Iowa.

In June, 1923, Jane Hinote, home demonstration agent in Cape Girardeau County, was selected by the State Club Office for three months to train demonstration teams throughout Missouri. The 1924 Annual Report says, "The team demonstration work was very popular. By actual count, 26 people of one county came 70 miles to the State Fair to see the local club teams demonstrate better farm and home practices. Another community, located more than 200 miles away, sent nine people with the county champion demonstration team to the State Fair. Practically all of the 23 demonstration teams were accompanied by delegations of home folks."

Only three members were selected in each county for training for competitive demonstrations with other counties.

Demonstrations became a part of the Junior Farmers' Week Program for the first time in 1915. That year, canning, making button holes, fancy stitches, plain stitches, and stringing corn for seed were demonstrated.

The canning demonstration was a "mock" demonstration. The entire demonstration was presented and explained in detail. The only thing lacking was the vegetables. In sewing, articles were shown, and the stitches explained with a chart.

In 1918 Olga Hungate, assistant state club leader, trained several teams and home demonstration agents together. Good demonstrations were then given in county contests and at the Southeast Missouri Fair at Sikeston and the Missouri State Fair at Sedalia. Canning teams representing Butler, Cape Girardeau, Dunklin, New Madrid, and Scott counties gave demonstrations in a tent at the Southeast Missouri District Fair in 1918 and 1919. The 1918 results follow:

Dunklin County, 1st;
Butler County, 2nd;
Cape Girardeau County, 3rd.

One finds the following in the 1924 annual report of the Extension Service: "Four-H club boys demonstrated how to grow early potatoes to the Oakville Community." Further potato work was carried on by the Oakville Boys' Potato Club, using certified northern grown seed to produce 210 to 257 bushels per acre of

James Sutherland, who gained national recognition for his electricity project, became an idea man for Westinghouse after college.

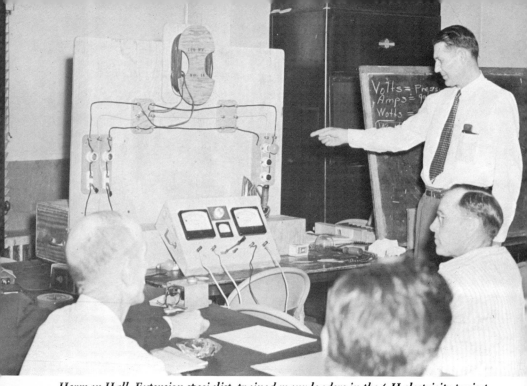

Herman Hall, Extension specialist, trained many leaders in the 4-H electricity project. (1951)

Tractor safety workshop at 1959 State 4-H Club Week. Tractor safety is stressed throughout the 4-H tractor program.

The men in work clothes are 4-H tractor maintenance leaders in training. Eight similar groups, totaling 201, participated in the training meeting that year. (1950)

St. Charles automotive group meets with their instructor. Front: Milton Kneemiller (leader) Dan Scherer, Cheryl Hrendell and Marian Dachroeden. Back row: Jim Lammert and Bob Barklage. (1963).

State champion agricultural demonstration team at the State Fair in 1924 and a participant in the Interstate Fair at Sioux City was comprised of Rawley Castel, Emery Castel, and Fred Stonner. Behind them are T. T. Martin of the State 4-H staff; Stewart Leaming, county agent; and Earl Page, Extension specialist.

Walter Wilkening, a 4-H member from Cape Girardeau County, is demonstrating at the first 4-H Tractor Clinic in Missouri, held in 1944.

Starting with a Sears gilt in 1949, George Barnitz had developed into a full-fledged breeder of Hampshire meat type hogs when this picture was taken in 1952 in Dent County.

A demonstration is selected each State Achievement Day to enter in the National Livestock Preservation meeting at Chicago during Club Congress. Sam Newby of Clinton County was the 1958 demonstrator.

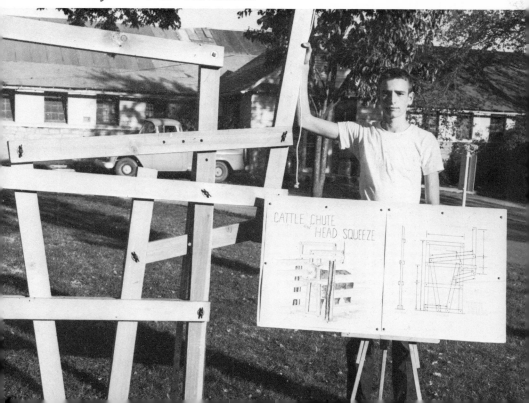

One of many double decks of Northwest yearling ewes distributed to 4-H members. This is a 1942 Linn County shipment.

Janice Warden has her 4-H allotment from a 1950 double deck shipment of yearling ewes to Daviess County.

Four-H members in the feeder pig project in south central Missouri helped change the character of pigs offered by Ozarks producers to Corn Belt buyers.

Producing good to choice beef with 25 bushels of corn or its equivalent is the objective of the young cattleman's five steer project. This project was started in Chariton County in 1942. Shown are: John Rush, county agent; Jack Dameron; and Warren Faris.

Previous to 1953, state 4-H livestock judging teams participated in the non-colligate livestock judging contest. The 1928 team included James Cason, Beverly Pace, and Charles Reid; all from Boone County. Also shown in the picture is T. T. Martin, state club leader, and James W. Burch, Extension animal husbandry specialist.

Members of the 1957 state meat identification and judging team were Jerry Goos, Lincoln; Charlotte George, Camden; Peggy Adams, St. Louis; and Eddie Stanek, Lincoln.

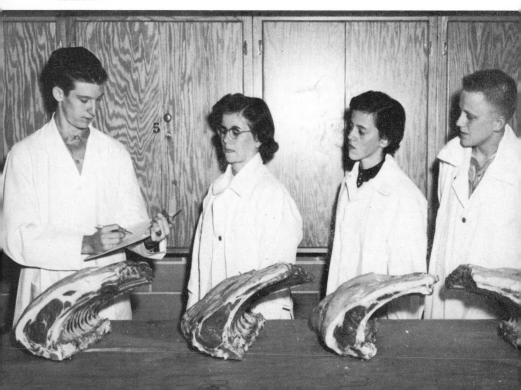

Exhibitors of champions at the 1956 Missouri State Fair included l. to r., Don Watts, Clarksville, champion 4-H Shorthorn; Russell Steinman, Albany, grand champion steer; Arthur Heath, Clark, champion 4-H Angus steer.

The 1948 Interstate top ton litter was raised by Warren Streeter, Sullivan County. Litter weight was 4770 pounds at 205 days.

Warren Lee Akins, Andrew County, proudly poses his champion Shorthorn at 1960 Interstate Show.

Showing the second place county group of five calves at the 1950 St. Joseph Interstate Baby Beef and Pig Club Show are, l. to r., Rose Alice Hopple, Hopkins; Martha Madden, Ravenwood; Velma Swartz, Marily Russell, and Curt Wakely, Graham.

Members of state livestock judging team in 1958: David Davenport, Gary Collins, Donald Anderson, and Dwight Roth, of Cass County. Horace Hunt, county agent is holding the calf.

D. Merrill Davis of Jackson, Ohio, is a popular song leader at numerous national 4-H assemblies, including Missouri State Club Week.

*Helen Marie Elliot,
Outerbelt 4-H Club of
Jackson County, poses
her five-gaited saddle mare.*

*Happy Valley 4-H Horsemanship group of Clay
County poses in 1958 picture.*

Four-H corn yield contests were popular in the forties. This is a Boone County 4-H corn project group with James Meyer who was associate county agent in Boone County at the time.

Lloyd Egger and John Hunziger of Holt County had the grand champion agricultural demonstration at the State Round-up in 1936. Hybrid corn has now displaced open pollinated seed corn.

Bernadine and Hildegarde Orf of St. Charles County gave this foods demonstration at Junior Farmer's Week in 1927.

Opal Caldwell and Dorothy Wilson, Caldwell County, composed the state home economics demonstration team in 1933.

Parents and leaders of the 4-H girls in the Brushy community, Henry County, are enjoying a dinner served by the girls at the end of their 1950 food preparation III project.

Alice Engelbrecht of the Ambrose 4-H Club, Cole County, stored 925 quarts of meat, vegetables, fruit, jellies, and relishes for her family in 1946.

Marilyn Maize of Harrison County is shown with her vegetable project in 1956.

Modeling dresses made in 1944 clothing projects are: Sue Broaddus, Randolph County; Shirley Evans, Jackson County; and Alma Chappell, Chariton County.

Lorene Hostetter, Jackson County, first Missouri representative to national dress revue, 1925.

Marilyn Reichect, Pemiscot County, winner of 1958 State Dress Revue.

Pictured in the 1964 State 4-H Dress Revue are Janet Timm, Cooper; Donna Crook, Platte; Jean Gay, Andrew; Sonja Parkinson, Barton; Karen Tunnell, Lawrence; and Judy Ray, Ralls.

Kay Bird of Dade County was an enthusiastic 1958 clothing project member.

Jessalle Mallalieu and Arthur Chappue of Jefferson County gave a dairy demonstration at the National Dairy Show at Indianapolis in 1925.

E. C. Adams, Jr., Jackson County (left) began to build a herd with a 4-H dairy heifer calf. By 1928 he had this 4-H herd of four. He later joined with his father to establish the Adams Dairies of Kansas City and St. Louis. A fellow dairy project member, Paul Jons, helps hold the animals, including Adams' foundation cow, right.

Rodney Garnett of Cole County started his 4-H dairy project with this heifer and built a dairy herd of ten registered artificially bred Holsteins by 1956.

Albert Reinhart, Newton County, developed a 4-H dairy herd. The foundation cow is at the left of her progeny. (1949)

Helen Meyer and Betty Hefferman of Pettis County gave this demonstration in Home Grounds in 1932.

Sandra Sue Sevier of Henry County is shown giving a demonstration on flower arrangement at 1950 District Round-up.

The More Attractive Homes judging team of 1937 included Dorothy Lafton and Kay Buchanan, Jasper County.

Lynette and Dorothy Oetting, Lafayette County, are shown working with their 1957 home improvement project.

Blue Ribbon Winners in the 1962 boys grooming contest included, right to left, Stanley Shaner, Clinton; John Mick, Cole; Gail Metter, Barton; Ortha Green, Pemiscot; Stanley Dobbs, Jackson; Jimmy Newson, Chariton; Jim Ramesdall, Lincoln; Phillip Hanson, Pike; Larry Whitfield, Pemiscot; Ron Davis, Audrain; and Jim McFadden, Lafayette.

Poultry demonstration team for Cape Girardeau in 1926 consisted of Leon Bowers and Edward Miller.

First six prize winners in the 1956 Chicken of Tomorrow contest were left to right: Doris Breedlove, Billy Lee Clemons, Martha Ann Davis, Clayton Hunton, Louis Scott, Max Wicker, and Walter Russell.

JR. CHICKEN-OF-TOMORROW CONTEST

SPONSORED BY:
- MO. POULTRY IMPROVEMENT ASSOCIATION
- MO. POULTRY COUNCIL

IN COOPERATION WITH:
- MO. COLLEGE OF AGRICULTURE
- STATE DEPT. OF AGRICULTURE & EDUCATION

Both talent and courage are required in the bee project.

Lake Springs 4-H Club of Dent County established a forestry plantation in 1949. Picture taken in 1951.

FOREST PLANTING

DEMONSTRATION

ESTABLISHED APRIL 13 — 1949
LAKE SPRING 4H CLUB ——— GEORGE BARNITS
Extension Service–Mo College Agriculture
Mo Conservation Commission

Health contestants at the 1930 State Round-up included: Lisa Leewood, Nodaway County, first in state (4th from left) and William Ross Bodenhamer, Johnson County, first in state and nation (6th from left).

Mr. E. Sidney Stephens, first chairman of the Missouri Conservation Commission presents 1947 Edward K. Love Wildlife Conservation Scholarships to: (l to r) Earnest Smith, Newton; Mary Ann Engelbrecht, Cole; Elain Baxter, Cedar; and James T. Davis, Harrison.

This square dance team was selected to appear on the 1953 National Club Congress program. The team was sponsored by the U.S. Rubber Company. All of the members were from the Central Howard Club in Howard County. Members of the group are: Vivian Kiepe, Morrene Hughes, Mary Stagle, Nancy Woodward, J. T. Mounter, Don Hudson, Donnie Moulter, and Howard Johnson.

The Cope 4-H Club of Daviess County erected beaded signs similar to this one on highways leading into Gallatin on the west, south, and north in 1955.

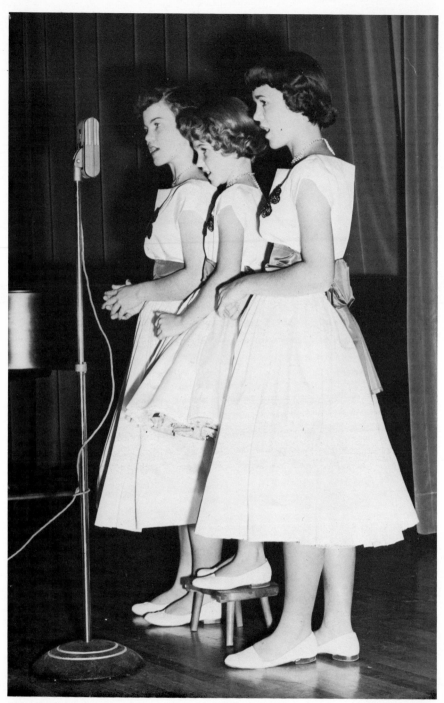

The Toalson Trio, Pauletta, Carolyn, and Kay Toalson of Polk County, participating in 1956 Share-the-Fun at State Achievement Day.

The Mitchellville 4-H Club of Harrison County has a long record of achievement in the wildlife conservation 4-H activity. Cecil Davis, conservationalist and 4-H leader, shows things of interest to Marilyn Youngman, Margaret Youngman, and Carolyn Crabtree. (1958)

Merlin Muhrer of Boone County demonstrates courtesies as he helps his mother with her coat. (1958)

Ronnie Powell, Randolph County, shows part of the safety series by placing a red flag pole on a tractor. (1957)

Jackson County 4-H band State Fair 1962

early potatoes. They accomplished this in spite of the fact that their fathers had told them it was not profitable to grow early potatoes. As a result of this example by youth, farmers planted early potatoes in following years and made good profits.

The Annual Report for 1924 says: "The county extension agent used club team to demonstrate hog sanitation." Ray County pig clubs have been an important factor in "spreading the gospel" of better production methods. Joe Shirkey, of Central Community, did splendid work. Starting early in the season, he met with his boys with regularity and taught them a great deal about hog raising.

He developed a demonstration team which attended the adult hog demonstration meetings and gave a practical demonstration on round worm prevention. This demonstration was a very effective means of teaching the lesson of disease prevention. The team went to the State Fair and made a splendid showing.

The pig club had a judging class coached by Mr. Robert Shirkey. The class learned much about judging and won prizes at the State Fair. Some of the boys have developed into practical hog breeders who can now compete in open classes with real success.

Demonstration teams of two were started about 1925. This was an improvement over teams of three members. Both individual members and teams of two have continued to demonstrate in clubs and on a contest basis since. Uniforms of different kinds have been used by team demonstrators since 1918.

At the close of 1927, the agents requested subject matter assistance in 4-H club work for the following year. The 4-H agents and subject matter specialists made plans for training leaders in subject matter and project work by demonstrations at conferences, and by specialists judging project work at county round-ups and fairs.

In 1929, some 5,916 members learned to judge the products which they produced. That year 4,933 members demonstrated farm and home practices which they learned in 4-H club work and 6,382 exhibited their own products. In addition, 5,600 members gave individual demonstrations of approved practices in regular club meetings. That year of 1929 saw 2,723 public team demonstrations.

In 1938, county demonstration days were held in several counties. By then the majority of counties were using one or several team demonstrations.

Although demonstrations by individuals had been used in club meetings since 1922, they were encouraged for the first time at district round-ups in 1943. This was because of the difficulties some teams had in getting together for practice. Gasoline shortage in those years was one of the main difficulties. Also, many subjects were better suited to one demonstrator, rather than two.

At the training meeting for county workers in 1945 and during the following year, the 4-H club staff and specialists used a modified plan of Job Instruction Training, known as the "J.I.T." procedure, to present project information and methods to agents. "J.I.T." was an improvement over the previous demonstration method. Agents then passed on this method of instruction to club leaders. It gave the leaders a greater feeling of assurance and satisfaction that they were giving the proper instruction in the right way.

According to Missouri county reports from 1946, a total of 543 training meetings—agriculture and home economics—were held for 4-H project leaders in 94 counties of the state with 4,809 leaders present.

In order that members might know quality products and strive to produce them, judging was included in club work in 1915. This was when corn judging contests were a definite part of the club program. Members of the grain judging, stock judging, sewing, and baking clubs participated in judging contests at the second Junior Farmers' Week, January 4-7, 1916, and at club fairs held in connection with the schools.

Judging soon became an important part of each project in Missouri. The standard club requirements for completion of club work were adopted and judging was one of the requirements.

The Interstate Fair at Sioux City, Iowa, held contests in stock judging. This added another incentive to the judging phase of 4-H work. Boys were taught standards by visits to livestock farms, where they saw outstanding purebred animals and heard them discussed by specialists and breeders. Members closely watched the judges and looked carefully at the livestock at such shows as the St. Joseph Baby Beef and Pig Show, the American Royal, and the State Fair.

Judging was taught at leaders' meetings through livestock classes and score cards. The club agent, county agent, or home demonstration agent then gave placings and reasons, and showed the classes so the leaders could understand the comparison.

The 1931 Annual Report of the Extension Service announced a new method of selecting judging teams. That year it was decided in the future to select a county-wide judging team in any 4-H club project which could represent a county in state contest.

A judging team consisting of three members in agricultural projects and two members in home economics projects would be selected in each local standard club with the project. The county judging contests would be open to all who wanted to compete, provided they represented standard 4-H clubs.

The highest ranking individuals of a project in the county judging contest were to become the "county-wide" judging team and be eligible to represent their county in state judging contests. The county judging team which won the state contest then would be eligible to represent Missouri in interstate and national 4-H judging contests.

By 1934 special judging days and special demonstration days were conducted in some counties. Both leaders and members took part in the training program. Special district judging days in dairy and livestock projects and county demonstration days were conducted by the county agents with the help of the state club staff and specialists, to give members and leaders technical knowledge in various phases of club instruction work. Special district conferences were conducted for home demonstration agents by the state club staff, and by specialists in home economics.

A year later, in 1935, district 4-H judging days were conducted in seven district meetings in two counties in Missouri during the first part of July. Some 1,074 members from 27 counties competed. The meetings were held at farms where quality livestock was available. T. A. Ewing and E. S. Matteson, Extension animal husbandry specialists, and M. J. Regan and Warren Gifford, Extension dairy specialists, were instructors for these training days.

In 1946, judging training in St. Louis County for members was conducted throughout the year in regular project meetings. Boys and girls learned to determine the value of their own products. Members and local leaders throughout the state attended the 4-H home economics judging days in July that year. Leaders were shown how to use judging as a teaching method, and as standards of types and perfection for the products produced in homemaking projects.

The use of the score card and how to give a set of reasons in judging were demonstrated. Techniques used in formal judging contests were also demonstrated.

Much more emphasis was put on judging in 1946 as an educational tool which resulted in improvements in standards. It also improved the ability of members to judge their products and to give reasons for their placing in judging. The members were learning not only to produce good products, but also how to judge products.

Now we see the part leadership has played and how it has been developed in all its phases throughout the years since 1914. No state or national program dealing with youth, has so responded to leadership at all levels as has 4-H.

Community Leadership . . . Project Leadership . . .
Junior Leadership . . . Home Economics Extension Club Leadership

Since 4-H club work began in 1914, voluntary local leadership has been the foundation stone on which this great program has grown all over America, and especially has this been true in Missouri.

The history and programs of Missouri's 4-H leadership system include the early-day teacher-leader phase in the public schools. This was followed by recruitment of leaders, largely from the residents of the many local communities under the guidance of the Extension Service in accordance with a plan known as the "group work" plan.

When the voluntary leadership program first started in Missouri, many local people were reluctant to give their full cooperation to one of their own number as leader.

As a result, at first, paid workers on other jobs often would work as leaders in their spare time. This extra service was rendered by teachers, ministers, Red Cross workers, nurses, secretaries, and clerks.

In time the objectives and procedures in club work became fully understood by local people, and when the local leaders had demonstrated their ability to lead and to help attain the group objectives, then these local leaders received full assistance from many others at the local level.

Missouri state and county club agents have noted that outstanding leadership usually is available in local communities at all levels of the culture. All it needs is to be discovered and trained. However, leadership does not remain in one place. Regardless of how well local leadership is developed, every local problem is subject to change. It is estimated that there are certain differences in probably one-fifth of the local population each year. These changes, or variations, take experienced leaders away from the community, and other leaders often quit because they feel that they cannot continue to devote their time and energy to the 4-H program.

This makes necessary the recruitment of new voluntary leaders. Constant recruitment is necessary also to provide leaders for growth.

During the voluntary teacher-leader school club period, rural youth activities were known as Boys' and Girls' Club Work. This period officially started in Missouri on March 1, 1914, and ended on November 30, 1921, when the Missouri school club plan was reorganized and superseded by the group work educational plan of the Extension Service.

At the close of the period, top leadership was provided by one state club leader and two assistant state leaders. There were 588 clubs with 8,177 members, many of whom were individual junior cooperators without being a part of any club group. There also were 558 local leaders, 95 percent of them being teachers.

Many teachers were away from the community in which they taught during the vacation or summer period. Because of this, many clubs were limited to activity only during the fall and winter months and there were few spring and summer clubs. The school plan of instruction in club meetings was emphasized in reports which showed the most pressing need of the teacher-leaders to be well illustrated charts for instructing club members.

Teacher-leader training meetings were held mainly during the fall and spring months. At these meetings the county Extension agents and home demonstration agents presented essential subject matter.

Usually the club programs for teacher-leader conferences included the following:

(1) Explanation of the Missouri club requirements.
(2) A typical demonstration club meeting, with the officers presiding.
(3) Club contests, events, and standards.
(4) Club literature, records, and reports.
(5) The spring achievement program.

Special training also was given to the teacher-leaders, often during the school term, through visits to club meetings and other activities, by state staff members and by the county superintendent of schools. Club members often were encouraged to complete their work by being offered additional school credit.

Leader training during the summer months often was presented as part of the program of judging days, tours, achievement days, and rallies.

During the second period of club development, the emphasis on leadership changed as the basic club organization changed. This began in 1921 and ended in 1938 with the start of the community 4-H club organization.

The overall club leadership situation in 1926 revealed the following:

(1) Club work was being carried on in 94 Missouri counties. There were 949 standard clubs, mostly project groups, with 8,994 members enrolled and 4,816 completing (53 percent). Also 95 Missouri counties held educational training meetings with 910 voluntary leaders taking part.

(2) One of the first Missouri counties to conduct an all-day training conference was Lincoln County. The meeting was held at Troy. Mrs. Clarence Cannon presided.

Other aspects of club leadership during that period were as follows:

(1) A new Missouri club charter was issued. This was in conformity with the National Standard Club Requirements adopted in Washington, D.C. in 1927.

(2)   A system of scheduling club events and procedures was set up, standardized on a state-wide plan, and adapted to local conditions.

(3)   Subject matter Extension specialists became more closely identified with the club program. This was especially true in the preparation of literature and in the educational training of local leaders. More stress was placed on approved practices.

(4)   A State 4-H Club Committee was formed. It recognized policy making and the establishment of goals and standards as a cooperative venture between County and State Extension Services. One of the questions raised by this joint committee was relative to the advisability of conducting the older youth program separate from the 4-H club program.

(5)   It was decided that the field work of the state club staff should follow the district plan provided for state Extension supervisors. A state 4-H club staff member was . assigned to each of the then existing five districts, but maintained an office in Columbia.

The first state-wide conference for local leaders was conducted in 1929 as a special section of the State 4-H Club Week, with W. H. Palmer, state club leader of Ohio, assisting in the program.

*   *   *

The educational training of local club leaders included the solving of various problems which grew out of the new club organization. The following usually became the new order of things:

(1)   Club organization including the new club charter and seal, club calendars, records and reports.

(2)   Judging and exhibiting club products, and demonstrating approved practices. Less emphasis was now placed on contests.

(3)   The all-around needs of boys and girls outside the scope of project work. Such things were considered as selected group activities for each club, a variety of recreational activities to fit different occasions, parliamentary procedures, and other program improvements based on interests of youth.

(4)   The local leaders' special problems were considered in "question and answer" periods, including tests of information in the form of games.

(5)   A small number of subject matter conferences were held. These were conducted either by the agents or specialists representing the state club staff.

At the close of the period in 1938, some 17 years after the beginning in 1921 on group work basis, the following was the leadership situation:

(1)   Some 57 counties in Missouri had developed county councils of leaders. These consisted of all adult club leaders and assistants, with the county Extension agents and home demonstration agents as ex-officio members.

Each council had officers and committees in charge. Most of the councils held quarterly meetings with a few counties holding two meetings, others six meetings, a few a dozen meetings.

A suggested form for a constitution and by-laws was distributed among the counties from the state club office, with the recommendation that it be adapted as needed to local situations.

(2)   In 1938, club work was being conducted in 111 counties of Missouri by 4,634 voluntary leaders, most of whom were farmers and homemakers. A total of 27,035 members were enrolled in 2,899 clubs in Missouri, mostly in project groups. About 75 percent completed. Of all 4-H members, 84 percent were enrolled in public schools, and 16 percent were not in school.

*   *   *

The adoption of the community type 4-H club organization in 1938 brought in a new club era in Missouri. It also was the cause of many changes in the leadership organization and training with the further specialization of literature and leaders. These may be summarized as follows:

(1)   About one-fourth more voluntary leaders were needed for the larger unit than had been necessary for the smaller project unit.

(2)   The need for junior leaders became more essential as a means of lessening some of the leadership load at the members' level of activity.

(3)   Also, the larger reorganized club unit system reduced the number of 4-H clubs by about one-fourth.

(4)   All-year-around clubs now became more necessary and more desirable as the proper setting for the enriched program of projects and group activities. By 1943, some five years after the reorganization took place, about 25 percent of all Missouri standard clubs were continuous organizations.

(5)   Under the new system, two sets of club meetings were provided for:

   a.   The general monthly meetings of all members and leaders with assistance.

   b.   Separate project meetings held at times and places best suited for teaching purposes.

   This change in kinds of club meetings produced the community club leader who was in charge of the general monthly meetings, while the specific project leaders served as teachers in the project meetings. Then the office of junior project chairmen was created. This gave an officer to preside over the separate project meetings.

(6)   Leaders with specialized project and group activity jobs soon were being trained in subject matter conferences:

   a.   In 1943, there were 1,517 project leader training meetings, and 848 conferences held for community club leaders. Some 5,800 leaders attended.

   b.   The club literature improved and became more specific. For the first time separate leaders' guides were developed for each project.

(7)   The Rural Youth program was developed with the organization and program separate from the 4-H club program. These groups had adult advisors instead

of local leaders. Each unit had its officers and committees, which were guided by a representative of the state club staff. Most of these Rural Youth organizations were on a community or district basis, but there were some county organizations. It took more than five years to reorganize the literature and the training system, and to get this information to the public.

(8) *Changes in State Leadership.* The following persons have been state 4-H project leaders in Missouri:

   a. R. H. Emberson served from 1914 until 1921, but remained on the state staff until December 1, 1942. He worked with non-agent counties.

   b. T. T. Martin served from 1923 until 1943 but remained on the state staff as state club agent until 1953. In this capacity he devoted much of his time to making practical 4-H club studies, training voluntary leaders, and teaching 4-H courses in summer schools.

   c. Robert S. Clough succeeded Mr. Martin as state 4-H project leader in 1943. He served until his retirement in 1958. Since then, Mr. Clough has done extensive research in preparation of this publication. He has devoted much time as a member of the Board of Directors of the Missouri 4-H Foundation, which he helped organize.

   d. Frank Graham succeeded Mr. Clough as state 4-H project leader in 1958, and continues in that position.

(9) *The Status of the Work in 1960.* In 1960, about 22 years after the community 4-H club was set up in Missouri, the status of leadership in 4-H club work can largely be determined from the following statements of growth, standards of training, and achievements:

   a. *4-H Club Statistics:* There were 36,807 members enrolled in the 114 counties of Missouri in 1960, including 3,103 Negro members, with 28,641 or 80.5 percent completing. There were 1,752 standard clubs (see p. 25 for standard club description) with white members, and 58 with Negro members.

   The average age of these members was 12.8 years. This age has remained virtually unchanged through the years. The total enrollment consisted of 54.1 percent of girls, 45.9 percent of boys. In the early days of club work in Missouri, about two-thirds of the members were girls, and a little more than one-third were boys. The enrollments of boys and girls tend to become more nearly equal as club work develops.

   b. *County Councils of Leaders:* In 1960, there were 103 county councils of voluntary leaders in Missouri. Some 1,229 meetings were held, with a total attendance for the year of 30,754 persons.

   These programs were planned by local committees and by local officers in charge, under the guidance of agents of the Cooperative Extension Service. In conducting their own self-help training and planning programs, they were living up to one of the high principles of group work.

   c. *The Annual Youth Leaders' Conferences:* There were one-day county conferences for project leaders. These were conducted on a uniform, state-wide basis. In 1960, the attendance was listed as 3,572 leaders, 263 agents, and 95 others.

The Theme: Building a Strong Project Program. Sub-topics included: Tools and Tasks of Project Leaders, Blueprint for a Project Meeting, and the Finishing Touch.

The annual series of training conferences was started in 1950. A total of 83 counties conducted all-day conferences in 1960, with 78 counties serving lunch for the project leaders as guests.

d.   *The 4-H Club Leaders' Short Courses.* Six two-day camp short courses were conducted in 1961 for the training of community voluntary club leaders, with a total attendance of 488 persons. This program was started in 1949, and has grown into a permanent system of leader training with the passing of the years.

By 1950 the place of the community 4-H leader in the 4-H club plan was deep-rooted. Community leaders are interested mostly in organization, structure, and program. They leave project supervision and teaching to project leaders of project groups within the community club.

It was recognized in the beginning that the most direct way to interest all members of 4-H is through community leadership. Early plans called for five or six training centers where voluntary 4-H leaders could get away from their home environment and devote two days to intensive training directed to program planning. Sponsors provide meals and lodging, so that this arrangement provides a vacation with little expense except for transportation. The training is planned so that all community leaders can be reached every three years.

The original camp conference plan was originated by the G.M. & O Railroad for eleven counties served by that railroad in the summer of 1949.

The first meeting of the Board of the Trustees of the Missouri 4-H Foundation could foresee making such training state-wide by securing sponsors for a full schedule of eight conferences in 1952. The number was reduced to six, and these have all been continued year after year. The 1952 schedule tells the story. Sponsors not mentioned in the 1952 schedule include Lester Cox for a Southwest Missouri group at Drury College one year, and the Pet Milk Company and others.[29]

Much credit is due to the Missouri State Park Board for use of facilities at Sherwood Forest and Frenchman's Bluff in Cuivre River Park; Bob White at Knobnoster; Clover Point at Lake of the Ozarks State Park; Camp Smokey at Roaring River State Park; Grand River in Crowder State Park, Trenton; Big Springs at Van Buren State Park; and Marvin Hillyard, St. Joseph.

e.   *District Junior Leaders' Conferences:* A total of five district junior leaders' conferences were conducted in 1960. The attendance was 518 junior leaders. These conferences were held at camps at Wappapello for the southeast area, Lake of the Ozarks for the central area, Roaring River for the southwest area, and at Crowder for northwest Missouri. The Missouri Bankers' Association and the Sears-Roebuck Foundation of Chicago were the financial sponsors of these training camps; in addition, each delegate paid a registration fee of $3.

[29]See Chapter 6, Junior Leader Conferences . . . Camps.

The training was supplemented by exchange visits of 4-H groups in Missouri to other states. Clay County groups have visited Beaver County, Oklahoma (1957), Christian County, Kentucky (1958), four Big Horn Counties in Wyoming (1959), and Nelson County, Kentucky (1960). Bates County groups have visited Greene County, Ohio (1963), and Iowa County, Wisconsin (1964). Chariton County groups have visited Hardin County, Kentucky (1962), and Charles Mix County, South Dakota (1963). Livingston County groups visited Clinton County, Ohio (1962), Perryton County, Texas (1962), and Lapeer County, Michigan (1963). In all cases there have been return visits. Many other exchanges are being planned.

Jack C. West, Extension youth agent, has this to say regarding the Clay County exchanges: "The Clay County Junior Leaders Club organized and carried out these trips, financing the programs with money-making projects. Participation in the programs varied from 17 to 37 members."

Junior Leadership was started as a regular club project in Missouri in 1948; in 1960, there were about 3,000 junior leaders enrolled in the state.

f.   *The 4-H Tractor Maintenance Clinics:* Beginning in 1945, with 57 leaders participating, annual tractor maintenance clinics have been conducted in Missouri by the Cooperative Extension Service. The financial sponsorship was provided by Standard Oil of Indiana. A total of seven two day clinics were conducted in 1960, with an attendance of 134 leaders who averaged 35 years of age. There also were 26 county agents and 84 others in attendance. Back in their local communities, these leaders led 528 members in their own tractor maintenance projects.

Practical instruction was given under the technical leadership of the Extension agricultural engineering specialists, who were assisted by technicians from the Standard Oil Company and from the local tractor dealerships who provided workshops, tools, and tractors for the sessions.

During the past 15 years, the Standard Oil Company has provided more than $1,000,000 in the sponsorship of this program on a nation-wide basis. This money was used for literature, expense of local leaders in attendance at clinics, and for educational trips and college scholarships of tractor members in cooperating states. The only compensation this company received for this service was good will.

g.   *District Conference of 4-H Dairy Club Leaders:* Dairy club leaders from 42 counties attended six all-day district farm training meetings in 1960. The program was conducted by the Missouri extension dairy specialists, the state club staff, and local dairymen. Such problems as judging, demonstrations, dairy herd records, and dairy club awards were discussed on the program. This dairy leaders training program has continued for two decades.

h.   *The 4-H Club Training Programs for Agents:* During 1960 4-H club training programs for agents were conducted as follows:

1.   District meetings were held by subject matter specialists in home

economics, clothing, foods, home management, dairy, electricity, livestock judging, and vegetables.

2. An agent's guide for "Three Meetings for Training New 4-H Leaders" filled a long-time need for definite agent training to guide the 4-H work of new leaders.

Junior Leaders Become a Part of the 4-H Club Organization

Mature 4-H members began serving as junior leaders in the twenties. The name had not yet come into use. It was not uncommon for a member of one club to organize and lead another club in a nearby community. They were actually juniors serving as adult leaders. Others assisted adult leaders in many ways.

The term "junior leaders" came into general use in the period along with the community club. The period of 1938 to 1948 is designated as unorganized "spot" service in junior leadership in this state. Junior leaders were pressed into service; they volunteered or "pinch hit" for adult leaders. These helping hands found many jobs to do on their own initiative.

Junior leadership became a project in 1948. Members enrolled in the project, moved out of the job or spot service phase to one involving purpose, plans, goal setting, methods, action, records, and achievement in leadership.

In 1962 a 4-H guide to leadership development was written by the state Extension staff. It contains a comprehensive plan for leadership development. All counties have access to this publication and have used it extensively. It has been most helpful in placing the responsibility for leadership training on the county basis and in the hands of the local Extension personnel.

Through these years the Missouri 4-H leader received information and training specific to the job which he or she carried out. This not only helped them become more effective in the work they do in the 4-H club, it assured greater personal satisfaction on the part of the leaders for the time and effort they spent on the program.

Four-H club leaders feel that learning and living are inseparable, and that all education is self-education. They feel that education should help one to interpret life, not merely provide club members with a collection of unrelated facts, but that it should aid the imagination and stimulate initiative, train the mind, enlarge the vision, develop the power to make sensible judgments, and help members to learn how to live and how to understand their fellow man.

Leaders of 4-H club work believe that to obtain these objectives, it is not only important to welcome individual initiative, but that it is also essential to arrange settings for stimulating group experiences.

4-H Leader Radio Recognition

"A Place in the Sun for 4-H Leaders," a radio recognition program was started June 1, 1951, by a committee of the Board of Trustees of the Missouri 4-H Foundation. It is still being programmed.

The original sponsor, Robertson's Farm Supply, Inc., East St. Louis, Illinois, is now in the 14th year of sponsorship. The original announcer for the program was

Charles Stuckey, formerly of KMOX and later of KXOK, both radio stations in St. Louis. The first leader recognized was Mrs. G. H. Henderson of the Stanley-Concord 4-H Club of Pemiscot County. The late A. W. Godfrey was manager, and J. W. Reid was president of Robertson's Farm Supply, Inc., at that time.

It has been from the beginning a joint program with Illinois 4-H Clubs. Programs have been broadcast on alternating weeks. The program was shifted to WEW in May, 1953, and to KMOX with Ted Manger, the farm director, in charge, in May, 1954. Junior leaders were given a place in the recognition in December, 1955. A total of 263 adult women leaders, 78 adult men leaders and 180 junior leaders from 47 counties have been honored in this way.

All Missouri counties touching Highway 63 and east, except eight, are included in the list of 47. Four counties are further west.

All leaders recognized have been given gifts, and all members of transcription parties have been entertained at luncheon.

Leaders from Kansas and Missouri shared in weekly programs on KFEQ at St. Joseph, Missouri, for a three-year period, 1952 to 1955. R. V. (Bob) Duncan, owner of Iowa-Missouri Walnut Company, was host and sponsor of this series. Members of the transcription parties were guests at the Robidoux Hotel and honored leaders were given gifts. Practically all of the counties in the St. Joseph trade territories of Kansas and Missouri were represented.

Leaders from most of the southwest Missouri counties were recognized in a similar manner on KWTO, Springfield, Missouri, in weekly broadcasts sponsored by the Union Stockyards Company. John Rush, president of the Company, was host, and Lloyd Evans was the announcer for these programs covering a two-year period, September, 1952, to September, 1954.

The Staley Milling Company sponsored a short program of 20 weeks for counties near Kansas City, Missouri, in 1954. Roderick Turnbull was the announcer for these programs on WDAF. A luncheon and gifts added color to the transcription parties they attended.

Leaders from more than 80 percent of the Missouri counties have been honored in four leader recognition programs.

Leadership Provided by Home Economics
Extension Clubs

T. T. Martin, former state leader of 4-H clubs, says, "The club itself is largely an outgrowth of community effort. It is sponsored locally by a community organization or committee."

In Missouri one of the community organizations sponsoring 4-H clubs has been the Home Economics Extension Clubs. They have given continuous support from 1928, when county councils were first organized, to the present time. They have been responsible for the organization of clubs in every county and in communities which Extension agents were unable to reach.

"Since the very beginning of club work, parents have been contacted and told of the value of the program, homes were opened for the organization of clubs, and leaders secured for both home economics and agricultural projects," says Amy Kelly, long-time member of the state Extension staff. "When members of 4-H clubs

This eight-state conference of state 4-H club staff members at Sioux City, Iowa, in 1944, included a number of the original state leaders (designated by *) dating back to 1914. Seated: A. J. Kittleson, Minn.; L. I. Frisbie,* Nebr.; R. A. Turner, Federal Extension Service; a representative of youth work in England assigned to Jamaica; Ranger McNeil, Wisc. Standing: Milo Uphdol, S.D.; Harry Rilling,* N.D.; Guy L. Noble, National Service Committee; Robert S. Clough, Mo.; J. Harold Johnson, Kans.; Paul Taff,* Ia.

Pictured at 1960 North Central State 4-H Leaders' Conference, Columbus, Ohio, (l. to r., seated): Hi Harshberger, Ohio; John Banning, Ind.; Harold Taylor, Ind.; Laurel K. Sabrosky, Federal Service; Leonard Harkness, Minn.; and Craig Montgomery, N.D. Standing: John Younger, S.D.; West Antes, Nebr.; Dick Lyons, Ill.; and Roger Regnier, Kans.; Russ Mawby, Mich.; Vern Varney, Wisc.; C. J. Gauger, Ia.; Frank Graham, Mo.

This unique picture includes three early leaders in the 4-H movement. A.B. Graham, second from left, is credited with being the organizer of the first 4-H Club in 1903, at Springfield, Ohio. R. H. Emberson, second from right, served as Missouri state 4-H leader from 1914 to 1923, and T. T. Martin, right, was Missouri state leader from 1923 to 1943. At left is one of the former members of Mr. Graham's original club.

The 1958 state 4-H staff included, l. to r., seated, Marian Beebe, Les Akers, Frank Graham, Charline Lindsay, Robert S. Clough, Katherine Saunders, secretary, and Arthur Ausherman and standing, John Burkeholder, Bill Colley, editor, Charity Bye Shank and Nelson Trickey.

Leaders' Camp, Marvin Hillyard, 1951.

Leaders at Crowder State Park Leader Conference in 1963.

Group at one of the 1950 community leader conferences, held at Union Electric Country Club in St. Louis.

Leaders' Camp Conference at Clover Point in 1952.

Jasper County delegation to community leaders' conference at Ginger Blue in 1952.

Leaders' camp conference at Clover Point in 1952.

Saline County group attending 1964 community leader conference at Bob White Camp.

Atchison County group attending 1960 community leader conference at Camp Crowder.

Buchanan County group attending 1960 community leader conference at Camp Crowder.

District Junior Leader Camp at Grande River in 1964.

moved off and the children needed assistance to continue the work. Home Economics Extension Club supplied the enthusiasm and morale necessary."

As would be expected, Home Extension Clubs with mothers of children in the age group 9-14 provided most of the leaders. However, a survey in Shelby County in the late 1940's showed 25 percent of the leaders were women without children or had grown children above 4-H age.

The subject matter leaders of the adult clubs who had been trained by specialists from the University of Missouri continued their work as teachers of 4-H members. Especially was this true of the clothing leaders. Many continued through six projects for six years.

In 1929 the Home Economic Extension Club Council decided it needed a guide in formulating its programs. This guide took the form of a Standard of Achievement. If a club met the requirements it was given a certificate. One of these requirements was the sponsoring of a 4-H club. Interpretation of sponsoring was worked out in several ways:

1. Assist the Extension agents in organizing new clubs.

2. Providing leaders in both subject matter and community activities.

3. If there was no 4-H club in the immediate vicinity of the Home Economics Extension Club, contact was made with the Extension agent to determine how it could help.

"Because of the interest of the Home Economics Extension Council and Clubs they became one of the supporting pillars of 4-H," Miss Kelly says. "The Extension agents took their difficult problems to them. One rather universal problem was the opening of the doors of the high school gymnasium for county-wide 4-H activities. Through the influence of a club member on the school board, or one who was a tax payer, the doors opened."

Funds were provided for children who could not go to 4-H Camp without some financial assistance. Money was provided for trips to county and state 4-H events.

As the 4-H club program increased its activities, the need for funds increased. The cost of the International Farm Youth Exchange Program and the National 4-H Conference caused help to be sought from the State Council of Home Economics Extension. The result was a "Nickel for Youth Work" for each Extension Club member.

Since 1962 approximately $500 for IFYE delegates and $400 for National 4-H Conference delegates have been given.

Home Economics Extension Clubs have no dues. Contributions are voluntary.

The community effort for the support of 4-H Club work has had the enthusiastic support of Home Economics Extension Clubs throughout the state. They feel both an obligation to the rural youth as well as pride in their accomplishments. "The old saying, 'Back of every movement for the benefit of the community is a woman' is in this instance the Home Economics Extension Clubs," Amy Kelly, long time Missouri Extension worker, says.

Chapter VI

4-H EVENTS

Events—whether at the big national shows, such as the International in Chicago, or the small community fair—are the true "show cases" of 4-H. At these fine events the public sees part of "the end product," what 4-H has been aiming toward, sees the bright-eyed youngsters at their best. These events, sometimes competitive, show 4-H in dress revue. Events are important and assist 4-H members toward the main goal—a finer, more glorious life in the future. Events, though, are only one of the 4-H "means to an end."

The following is an outline of 4-H events, beginning with the ones of international significance, and continuing down to the very small but very important community events:

I. International
   1. International Livestock Exposition
   2. International Farm Youth Exchange

II. National
   1. National 4-H Conference
   2. National 4-H Congress
   3. National 4-H Citizenship Short Course
   4. American Youth Foundation Camp
   5. National Dairy Show
   6. National Dairy Conference and Tour
   7. Junior Fact-Finding Conference
   8. National Safety Council
   9. 4-H Grain Marketing Clinic and Tour
   10. American Institute of Cooperation
   11. 4-H National Poultry Judging Contest
   12. National Junior Vegetable Grower's Association
   13. 4-H Livestock Conservation Demonstration
   14. American Royal Show
   15. Other 4-H Participation

III. Interstate or Regional
   1. American Royal Conference (4-H)

    2.   American Royal Livestock Show
    3.   Sioux City Interstate Fair
    4.   St. Joseph Baby Beef and Pig Show (4-H)
    5.   St. Joseph Dairy Show (4-H)
    6.   Market Days (4-H)
    7.   Regional 4-H Tractor Driving Contest
    8.   Regional 4-H Camp

IV. State
    1.   State 4-H Club Week - State 4-H Council
    2.   State 4-H Achievement Day
    3.   Junior Farmers' Week
    4.   State Fair
    5.   State 4-H Round-up
    6.   Lincoln University Short Course (4-H)
    7.   4-H Turkey Show
    8.   4-H Junior Leader Camp Conference
    9.   Conservation Camp Conference (4-H)
    10. 4-H Health Camp Conference

V. District
    1.   District 4-H Achievement Day
    2.   4-H District Fairs and Shows
    3.   Young Cattlemen's Day
    4.   Camps

VI. County
    1.   County 4-H Achievement Day
    2.   County 4-H Fairs
    3.   4-H Sunday
    4.   County 4-H Recognition Night
    5.   Other County Events

VII. Community

A Memorable 4-H Event

The following anecdote was related some years ago by an Extension worker.

Ervin Brune, a Jackson County 4-H member in the 1930's, was a polio victim. Ervin wore braces on both legs. This handicap, however, did not keep him from meeting all of his 4-H challenges. Other 4-H boys began calling him "Old Erv," completely in affection, and not in ridicule.

Ervin read the program for the Jackson County 4-H Fair to be held at Oak Grove about the time he was eleven years old. He noted that a terrapin race was scheduled. "Great," he said, "that's something I can do."

Erv began collecting terrapins with enthusiasm and promoted what he called his "Derby" by collecting and giving other club members terrapins for entry.

The race was staged by placing all the turtles under a wash tub at the center of a large chalk-marked circle. The tub was removed—that started the race in earnest. Prodding and coaching were not allowed.

Ervin trained his own entry, "Ben Hur," hard to win but when Ben Hur came through Ervin was embarrassed at having promoted the race which his own entry won. He laughed it off with a glance at his own legs, saying, "Did you know that this is the first race I ever won?" Ervin won many races after that—he won races for people's hearts and enjoyed every second he spent in 4-H club work.

Events, such as 4-H achievement days, and all the others, provide a means whereby members can compare their accomplishments — their growth in 4-H — with others. These events become the fulcrum, the spring board, to greater things. Abraham Lincoln once said that he truly "began to become a lawyer" only after losing a case to a polished Cincinnati attorney, a graduate of Harvard, and he learned by comparing his own unpolished methods with those of the polished and successful lawyer.

"Events in 4-H club work can do much to broaden and polish the 4-H member," says Charline Lindsay, who has spent many years as a Missouri Extension worker in 4-H work. "The real reasons for holding 4-H events are to provide for the members, (a) an evaluation process, whereby they can compare themselves and their work with their fellows; (b) a learning process; (c) opportunity for achievement; (d) recognition of achievement; (e) opportunities for broader experience; (f) raise aspirations, and (g) develop understanding.

International Events

International Livestock Exposition

4-H members have had a place in the Chicago International since 1919 when the nucleus was formed for the National 4-H Club Congress, now in its forty-third year. Members have paraded in the arena at the Coliseum on Wednesday night of the show so long that it has become traditional.

The National 4-H Livestock Judging Contest, participated in by state teams throughout the nation, has had a prominent place in the big show's program.

Visiting the exhibits, watching the judging of livestock in the ring, and the horse shows in the afternoons and evenings are all memorable events.

The 4-H Sheep Shearing Contest is held in the sheep judging arena of the Exposition. Missouri has participated many of the years.

Many of these farm lads have taken occasion to give one of the Clydesdales on the six horse hitches a pat on the head and neck as members mingled with horses awaiting entrance to the arena.

Running concurrently with the International Livestock Exposition has been the National 4-H Club Congress, which is quartered in and held at the Conrad-Hilton Hotel. When the first national meetings of "Corn and Pig Club Boys" and "Canning Club Girls" were held in Chicago in 1919 most of the some 300 in attendance were quartered in the Blackstone Hotel, and the time was mostly spent at the stock show; Art Institute; Marshall Fields (world's biggest store); Sears-Roebuck; Wilson, Armour, and Swift packing plants; and browsing through Lincoln Park.

There was no "hard and fast" daily program as today. State club leaders mapped each day's program, often letting members of state delegations decide which place of interest to include for each day. Such men as Thomas E. Wilson, who until his death, worked tirelessly for club work, saw to it that each day's program at the first Chicago meeting in 1919 was filled to overflowing for eager-eyed farm boys and girls.

International Farm Youth Exchange (IFYE)

The International Farm Youth Exchange is known around the world as the international phase of the 4-H program. It is in effect a people-to-people program, known as IFYE.

IFYE delegates spend nearly six months with host farm families in foreign countries mostly on other continents. Likewise, young people from cooperating countries live for like periods with farm families in this country.

The contractual relationship of the IFYE Program is between the U. S. State Department and Missions in various countries. All delegates must have been 20 years old or older when they were selected. Most Missouri IFYE alumni were farm-reared, and most host families for delegates coming here from other countries must be or have been farm families. About two-thirds of the IFYE alumni are now graduates of some college or university, and some have advanced degrees.

Orientation and supervision of both outbound and inbound IFYE delegates was done by the Federal Extension Service until it was assumed by the National 4-H Center in Washington. These agencies maintain contacts with visited countries throughout the stay of delegates. The State Extension Service does the follow-up on delegates coming to this nation.

Sentiment for developing a peace and goodwill program by older 4-H members was spontaneous following World War II. Delegates to the National 4-H Conference, resumed in 1946 after a lapse of four years, and delegates to National 4-H Club Congress following the war, after much discussion and counselling, were responsible for starting IFYE in 1948.

Missouri 4-H clubs did not participate in the 1948 programs. One delegate participated in 1949, none in 1950, one in 1951, and since that time, three to six outbound IFYE's have become "grassroots ambassadors" every year. Missouri has 55 IFYE alumni, covering 1949 through 1964.

About half of the financing for delegates comes from state and half from national sources. A very high percentage of the state fund has been produced through the efforts of 4-H members, leaders, and parents. Since 1952, 4-H delegates to State 4-H Club Week have sponsored one delegate each year. Outbound delegates have lived with families from the following countries or areas:

> 13 countries in Europe
> 4 countries in the British Isles
> 10 countries in Central and South America
> 2 countries in the Near East
> 3 countries in the Far East
> 2 Australia and New Zealand
> 1 Puerto Rico
> 35 Total

One hundred three inbound delegates from 43 countries have lived with Missouri farm families, including all of Continental Europe, most of Central and South America, India, Pakistan, Japan, Burma, Nepal, Taiwan, Philippines, Iran, Egypt, Turkey, Israel, British Isles, Jamaica, Ceylon, and Puerto Rico.

Returning delegates have presented slide-illustrated programs to thousands in Missouri. Each delegate has contacted hundreds in his overseas host country. Inbound delegates have made acquaintances with hundreds in Missouri farm homes and at gatherings.

National Events

National 4-H Club Conference

The first National 4-H Club Camp was held in Washington, D.C., in June, 1927. Four delegates, two boys and two girls, were selected on the basis of outstanding 4-H records. The first camp was on the lawn north of the original U. S. Department of Agriculture Building. Later it was moved to the banks of the Potomac River, south of the Washington Monument.

During attendance at this camp in 1941, delegates were told that Hitler had declared war on Russia. The Japanese attack on Pearl Harbor followed in December. The camp site was soon occupied with temporary buildings following the outbreak of World War II. Because of the war, no camps were held from 1942 through 1945.

In 1946, the delegates were housed in Navy barracks on Washington's Nebraska Avenue, and meetings were held on campus of American University. Temporary government buildings at Arlington Farms were the setting for the 1947 conference. Raleigh Hotel in Washington, D. C., was club headquarters from 1948 through 1958.

From 1959 to present, the National 4-H Center has been the conference home. It was the need for a central meeting place that caused the founders to purchase a college campus for a National 4-H Center. The name was changed from National 4-H Club Camp to National 4-H Club Conference in 1958.

The dates for holding the National Conference were changed from June to April in 1960. The Missouri Room was dedicated by the 1961 delegation that year.

More than half of the delegates each year are enrolled in college or are graduates. Some former delegates now have masters degrees, and at least four have doctorates. They live in 17 states — Connecticut to California, Wisconsin to Florida. More than 80 percent are residents of Missouri.

National 4-H Club Congress

The National 4-H Club Congress, now in its 43rd year, is America's greatest event dedicated to the recognition of youth's achievements. Some 1,200 youngsters, 14 years of age and older, assemble in Chicago following Thanksgiving Day. All 50 states and Puerto Rico are represented by official delegates who have been carefully selected on basis of merit and character.

The program begins on Saturday and continues through to the final party the next Thursday. Donors, Extension personnel, and visitors from all over the earth increase the delegations to some 1,500 in attendance by week's end.

Since 1944, the Conrad Hilton Hotel in Chicago has been headquarters for the 4-H club delegation. Almost all delegates are registered there. The 4-H club Congress has become the 4-H "show-window" of America through the facilities of printed and electronic words and pictures.

In the early years of 4-H a large number of delegates to the Club Congress were only partially sponsored. Today all Missouri 4-H delegates are fully sponsored for such necessary expenses as registration, travel, board and lodging. Missouri is given a delegate quota. In 1964 it was 32. A total of 1,205 Missouri members of 4-H have attended Club Congress from 1925 through 1964. Indications are that the figure will exceed 1,400 by 1970. Previous to 1925 the records are incomplete.

National 4-H Citizenship Short Courses[30]

The National 4-H Citizenship Short Courses started in 1959. Since 1960 one or more bus loads of Missouri club members have attended one of the summer sessions. By 1964, 1,298 members had attended one of the week-long sessions at the National 4-H Center in Chevy Chase, Maryland. Delegates are individually or community sponsored.

American Youth Foundation Camp

This Foundation, begun in 1924, has served youth in an outstanding character building program since its start. William H. Danforth, St. Louis, Missouri industrialist, served as president since its founding and continued in that capacity until his death on Christmas Eve, 1955.

The American Youth Foundation Camp is not a 4-H institution. However, members of 4-H have been included since 1938. The camps last two weeks. One is for older girls and another for older boys. It is held on the shore of Lake Miniwanca in Michigan.

Missouri's quota has usually been two girls and two boys. Up to 1964, some 95 Missouri members of 4-H have had the unique experience afforded by the camp. Delegates are selected for good records and in addition high standards in four-square living which includes all aspects of physical, mental, social, and spiritual fitness.

National Dairy Show

Dairy project members have participated in the National Dairy Show or Dairy Cattle Congress at Waterloo, Iowa, or both, since 1920. Provisions were made for participating in exhibiting, demonstrations, and judging.

Missouri members made many entries in 4-H dairy classes when the show was held in St. Louis. Farther removed sites have had few or no Missouri exhibitors. Demonstrations in both production and use were included continuously from 1925 to 1954. State dairy judging teams have participated in the National Dairy Judging Contest since 1920. Members enrolled in food preparation were eligible to demonstrate in the use of dairy products.

---

[30]This important 4-H event is described more in Chapter VII.

National Dairy Conference and Tour

The National Dairy Conference and Tour sponsored by the dairy industry started in 1955. Four to six Missouri delegates have a rewarding experience in their four-day sponsored trips to Chicago, Illinois. Both dairy and foods project members participate.

Junior Fact-Finding Conference

A Junior Fact-Finding Conference has provided educational experiences for poultry project members since 1954 when the parent organization, Poultry Fact-Finding Conference, included youth, or young adults. The conferences have been weekend meetings at Kansas City, Missouri. Up to 1964, some 44 Missouri members of 4-H had taken part in these sessions.

National Safety Council

Sixteen 4-H members who have made outstanding records in the 4-H safety activity have been delegates to the National Safety Council from 1955 to 1962. They have made valuable contributions to the sessions.

4-H Grain Marketing Clinic and Tour

Some 18 crops project members of 4-H attended the Grain Marketing Clinic and Tour during the eight years, 1954 - 1962. The clinic is sponsored by the Chicago Board of Trade. Meetings are held in the host city.

American Institute of Cooperation

Sixteen members interested in cooperatives have been delegates to the AIC during the period 1953 - 1964. Members have participated in conferences at the following land grant colleges: University of Missouri-Columbia; Colorado State University, Fort Collins; University of Illinois, Champaign; Ohio State University, Columbus; University of Nebraska, Lincoln; and Michigan State University, East Lansing.

National Poultry Judging

The National 4-H Poultry Judging Contest is held at Chicago. It is not a part of the National 4-H Club Congress but is conducted during that event.

National Junior Vegetable Growers Association

The National Junior Vegetable Growers Association was organized in 1943. The annual meeting program included demonstrations, judging, and exhibits. Missouri 4-H members enrolled in vegetable projects were active in the 1940's. Delegates attended meetings at Jackson, Mississippi; Detroit, Michigan; Washington, D.C., and New Orleans, Louisiana.

Livestock Conservation Demonstration

Livestock Conservation, Inc. of Chicago sponsored 4-H livestock conservation demonstrations for 12 years, up to and including 1963. Individuals or teams of two were eligible to participate. Most of the participating demonstrators from Missouri placed in the blue ribbon group.

American Royal Livestock Show

Meat animal 4-H project members have had an important place at the American Royal Livestock Show in Kansas City, Missouri, since the early 1920's. The 4-H exhibitors have come largely from Missouri, Kansas, Oklahoma, and Texas. A limited number are from Colorado, Iowa, Nebraska, and Illinois, with an occasional exhibitor from other states. Classes have been offered to 4-H members in cattle, sheep, and swine.

Future Farmers of America, better known as FFA, classes followed the same classification as the 4-H section of the show. The champions and reserve champions were declared champions of the junior show.

An invitational 4-H Livestock Judging Contest was included in the program in the early twenties. It developed into a contest involving most of the West Central States and many Southern States.

It is now practice for the runner-up to the state 4-H Livestock judging team that competes at the International Show in Chicago to represent Missouri at the American Royal Contest.

Meat Identification and Judging is another important 4-H feature of the American Royal program. Missouri has participated with a team of four since 1951. It has been largely a contest among teams from Missouri, Nebraska, Oklahoma, and Kansas.

A banquet is held each year for 4-H livestock and meat judging contestants on Friday evening before the formal opening of the show.

Other Participation

1956 - Pat Copperfield, Nodaway County, was selected as one of four 4-H members to be a delegate to the 11th National Conference on Citizenship in Washington, D. C., in September, 1956. This organization was sponsored by the Department of Justice and the N.E.A. until 1954 when it was granted a charter by Congress. It is dedicated to the development of more active, alert, enlightened, conscientious, and progressive citizenry in our country.

The conference credited the 4-H delegation with having made a worthy contribution. Moreover, the delegation left a favorable impression of 4-H with the 800 representatives.

1957 - Marion Scott, Jasper County, was selected from the entire girls' delegation to the 1957 National 4-H Club Conference for a New York radio appearance and a national magazine feature story.

1948 - Don Rutter participated in the National Sheep Shearing Contest at the International Livestock Exposition in Chicago.

1957 - Tim Guse, Jefferson County, participated in the 4-H Sheep Shearing Contest at the International Livestock Exposition in Chicago.

Regional and Interstate Events

American Royal 4-H Conference

The American Royal 4-H Conference is a three-state conference in Kansas City with a quota of 150 delegates each from Kansas, Missouri, and Oklahoma. In addition, there have been large delegations from Arkansas, some from Iowa and Nebraska, and an occasional delegate, or visitor, from other states.

Registration of delegates is completed on Sunday morning after the opening of the American Royal Livestock Show on Saturday. The program begins with an assembly followed by a tour of the city on Sunday afternoon. It closes with a banquet on Tuesday night. Tours, a visit to the American Royal Livestock and Horse Show, parties, and assemblies of delegates constitute the program. Delegates preside at assemblies, hear outstanding speakers, and participate in discussion of relevant topics of the day. Kansas City is the host.

The Cudahy Packing Company sponsored two American Royal delegates for many years but ended its program participation in 1963.

Folger's Coffee Company has sponsored a Missouri group consisting of foods delegates, one from a county since 1952 to the American Royal Livestock Show.

Breakfast for these delegates was a program highlight. Folgers began providing a breakfast for the entire Missouri delegation beginning in 1965.

Most of the delegates pay their own travel expenses, as well as lodging, and some meals. A banquet at the Muehlebach Hotel in Kansas City has been a feature of this annual affair. Often 4-H Share-the-Fun members have furnished the entertainment. The conference is a popular one with delegates. While this event is not staged as elaborately as the 4-H Club Congress in Chicago, it does provide a very rewarding experience for many more Missouri young people.

The Extension Service's Annual Report of 1925 first mentioned an American Royal delegation. That report said:

"Missouri was represented by about 100 club members, who exhibited a large number of hogs and a number of baby beeves, took part in the poultry and meat demonstration contests or attended as county club delegates. A marked improvement was made in developing organized club group activities which were featured at banquets, on tours, and in daily assemblies. Everything points to the development a fine program at Kansas City, in the 'Heart of America', during the next five years."

In 1926, however, efforts to conduct an American Royal Conference were disappointing, and no mention is made of it from 1927 until 1933, when the record shows 200 official delegates. From 1933 until World War II the delegates, largely exhibitors and contestants, held banquets and made tours.

The conference was not held in 1945, but was resumed in 1946, when it was set up on a quota basis. Counties were given a quota and delegates were selected within the county. It was at that time that the plans of 1925 were finally realized, and the program pattern now in use was adopted.

Credit should be given to the leaders of the four states for planning the program and to the late Walter Atzenweiler, manager of the agricultural committee, Kansas City Chamber of Commerce, for securing sponsors; and directing the 4-H club activities.

Sioux City Interstate Fair

The first opportunity for Missouri 4-H members to compete with members of other states was provided by the Sioux City Interstate Fair. This event began in 1920 and continued through 1936, some 16 years. Missouri first participated in

1920. Eleven states took part: Iowa, Illinois, Wisconsin, Minnesota, North Dakota, Nebraska, Kansas, Colorado, South Dakota, Montana, and Missouri.

The fair was a tremendous educational and personal experience for all who had the opportunity to experience it.

St. Joseph 4-H Baby Beef and Pig Show, and Sale

The St. Joseph 4-H Baby Beef and Pig Show and Sale began in 1920 as a part of a stocker-feeder show.

The first year it was limited to northwest Missouri Counties. Four counties had entries. Classes were offered on junior yearling steers and heifers by breeds. Carlot and county group of five classes were added in 1925. The home-owned class was offered for the first time in 1955. Thirty-three calves from four counties were shown the first year. In 1923, some 300 calves from 16 counties were shown. The pig show was added in 1926.

Harry Garlock was made superintendent of the show very soon after it began. He continued to serve in this capacity until he retired as vice-president of the St. Joseph Stockyards Company in 1960. All of the administrative staff of the Stockyards Company, including the presidents, have taken a personal interest in this show and made valued contributions to its success.

Many of the stockyards employees have served long and well in their several capacities of helping with this event.

The classification for exhibitors has not changed since 1945. It follows:

Light and medium weight baby beef in three breeds; Angus, Hereford and Shorthorn. The breaking point between light and medium weights being arrived at mathematically to equalize numbers in the two weight classes.

A home-owned class. All breeds and weight within the age limits are shown in this class. Calves dropped on the home farm to be eligible for this class.

A country group of 5 steers.

A carlot (15) from a county.

Champion and reserve champions by breeds. First and second prize home-owned animals are included.

Grand and reserve champions of the show.

After the first year of the show in 1920, all Missouri counties north of the Missouri River and west of Highway 63, less Randolph and plus Saline and Lafayette, were included in this popular event. Very early in the development of the show many Iowa, Kansas and Nebraska Counties had entries.

County groups of five and carlots were first exhibited in 1925. As single entries increased, the classification enlarged to three breeds and two classes of each breed on a weight basis. The home-owned Class was added in 1945 — all breeds eligible.

There is a limitation to the number of entries permitted from a county. In addition, a sifting committee sends to the St. Joseph Stockyards any animal considered an unworthy show animal. On some occasions this resulted in "busted"[32]carlots. The number of carlots in the beef show range from 10 to 20, with Missouri consistently exceeding the totals from the other three states. Champions and blue ribbon winning steers are paraded at the city auditorium on Wednesday evening of the show. The animals are sold at auction on Thursday of show week.

While 4-H swine breeding exhibits have not often had the spotlight, St. Joseph, at the heart of a great corn-producing section, has one of the finest 4-H shows for market hogs in the nation. This is an inter-state show. Exhibitors from sections of four states are eligible, including Missouri, Kansas, Nebraska, and Iowa.

Traditionally classes have been offered for single barrow, pens of three barrows, ton litters, and county groups of five pens of three barrows. While four states are eligible, this has been largely a Missouri show.

Stimulus has been given to this project by the "ton-litter" exhibit. In this contest, members are required to feed a litter to a ton weight in 180 days in order to qualify. Originally awards were made on ton litters on the basis of 40 percent for conformation and type, and 60 percent for average daily litter gain. The percentage was later reversed as the lard-type hog began to wane in general popularity and the meat-type hog became the favorite.

In 1945, Paul Allen Clark of Andrew County exhibited 16 Chester Whites that weighed an even 4,000 pounds in 210 days.

That year 37 litters were exhibited. Thirty-six of them were from Missouri farms. The weights of the ton litters reached an all-time high when Warren Streeter of Sullivan County in 1948 with 15 Spotted Poland-Hampshire crossbreds achieved 4,720 pounds at 205 days. Twenty-four litters qualified that year for this class. Seventy litters qualified in this class in 1946.

"Economical pork production is wrapped up in one package in the "ton litter" project at the St. Joseph event. Selection for type and fecundity, feeding, and overall management play an important part in the total program," says Don K. Spalding, president of the St. Joseph Stockyards Company.

The City of St. Joseph has supported this show for over 40 years but the rank and file of citizens did not see the show as it was held at the stockyards in South St. Joseph. So in 1944, they brought the show downtown. They exhibited the champion animals on the floor of the St. Joseph Auditorium-even the champion ton litters. St. Joseph responded and filled the auditorium year after year.

A feature of the Wednesday evening show is the presentation of the Interstate Boy and Girl. While major attention is centered on livestock, a display of home economics exhibits is sponsored by the women's division of the Chamber of Commerce. This is another downtown attraction that has added very much to this 4-H event.

St. Joseph Dairy Show

The St. Joseph agriculture program has staged an Interstate 4-H Dairy Show since 1944. It involves the states in the St. Joseph trade territory. It is an excellent show with a full classification for all dairy breeds.

---

[32]When the carlot number was reduced due to failure of one or more calves to qualify because of quality, the common terminology "busted" was used to describe it.

St. Louis Beef Show and Sale

The East St. Louis Livestock Exchange started a junior beef show and sale in 1927. This event was terminated during World War II.

Also in 1927 the Producers Livestock Marketing Association, East St. Louis, promoted a junior baby beef show and sale. This event also was terminated during World War II. Shortly thereafter, Producers started the sponsorship of Missouri-Illinois 4-H Beef Marketing Days at which the calves were sorted into lots uniform in weight, type, and quality and sold on the open market. This sale has been continued until the present.

Lamb Marketing Days

Lamb marketing days have been held at St. Louis and St. Joseph for many years. The Kansas City market has sponsored a lamb marketing day some of the years. The lambs were graded into prime, choice, and good grades and sold through regular market channels. During the forties and fifties many county shows and sales were held. Lambs moved directly to market after local grading. Lamb marketing days enabled 4-H members to see market procedures at close range.

Regional Tractor Driving Contest

Many minds contributed to achieving a program which focused on skills, safety, and economy in the tractor project.

Three events made up the 4-H tractor contest. The first event involved using a tractor to pull a four-wheel implement and to move it from one parking stall to another parking stall adjacent to it. The second driving event involved the use of a tractor to pull a two-wheel implement through a winding obstacle course. The combination of the two driving events was used to demonstrate the ability of a 4-H tractor driver to operate skillfully and safely. The third event associated with the tractor driving contest was a practical pre-check of a tractor before starting to do a day's work.

To encourage participation, tractor driving contests were set up in many counties with the winner participating in a state tractor driving contest held at the Missouri State Fair. Later, the state driving contest was moved to the University of Missouri campus in Columbia and conducted as a part of State Achievement Day.

The first regional tractor driving contest involving 25 West Central states was held at the Kansas State Fair in 1957. Other regional events have been held in Illinois (1958), Missouri (1959), Michigan (1960), Texas (1961), Ohio (1962), Oklahoma (1963), and North Dakota (1964).

Regional 4-H Camp

Starting in 1948 a regional camp for Negro 4-H club members was held for Southern states. The program was similar to the National 4-H Conference held at Washington, D. C., each year.

This event was discontinued in 1961. Negro delegates are now participating in Missouri 4-H Achievement Day, Club Congress, and the National 4-H Conference in Washington, D. C.

State Events

State 4-H Club Week

The first annual Missouri 4-H Club Week was held on the University of Missouri campus in Columbia on June 6-9, 1946. A total of 632 boys, girls, leaders, and Extension agents from 93 Missouri counties attended.

Club Week is held for the purpose of recognizing achievements of members and to acquaint them with the University of Missouri as well as to help them to make new friends and to accept new ideas and information. The program is aimed at giving recognition to leaders for outstanding accomplishments. The first 4-H Club Week was also the first state 4-H event held in Missouri in which there were no contests.

The original objectives of 4-H Club Week have not been changed since the event began in 1946. These objectives have best been stated by Miss Jane Hinote[33] as follows:

(1) To recognize achievements of members.

(2) To acquaint members with their state university.

(3) To make new acquaintances.

(4) To get new ideas and information.

(5) To inspire members and leaders to greater 4-H achievements.

Citizenship has been an important theme of State 4-H Club Week. Programs have varied but always included talks, discussions, singing, tours, workshops, recreation, election of State 4-H Council officers, and a citizenship ceremony. General assemblies are presided over by 4-H members.

Program themes each year for 4-H Club Week have been as follows:

1946 - America's Share in Maintaining Peace
1947 - Working Together for a Better Home and World Community
1948 - Better Homes Today for a More Responsible Citizenship
       Tomorrow
1949 - Better Living For a Better World
1950 - Better Living For a Better World
1951 - Citizenship Challenges Youth
1952 - Developing Good Citizens Through 4-H
1953 - Working Together for World Understanding
1954 - Improving Family and Community Living
1955 - Improving Family and Community Living
1956 - Improving Family and Community Living
1957 - The Challenge of Peace
1958 - Preparing Today for Living Tomorrow
1959 - Live - Learn - Lead
1960 - Learn - Live - Serve

---

[33] Miss Hinote, now retired from the University of Missouri Extension Service, was one of the first women employed to work with club youth in Missouri and the nation, and for years was a member of the state staff in Columbia. Considerable help in preparation of this manuscript came from her.

1961 - Learn . . . Live . . . Serve
1962 - Learn . . . Live . . . Serve Through 4-H
1963 - 4-H Citizenship in Action
1964 - 4-H Citizenship in action

In addition to state and federal Extension staffs, many people have contributed to the high standard of State Club Week programs. Most of these are nationally known. A partial list follows:

Former President Harry S. Truman.
Governors of Missouri.
Mr. Paul C. Jones, U. S. Congressman, Kennett.
The Presidents, Vice-Presidents, and Chancellors of the University of Missouri.
The Deans of the College of Agriculture and Extension Division.
Col. C. R. Stribling, President, Mexico Military Academy, Mexico.
Dr. Ed Aiton, Director of 4-H Club Work, Federal Extension Service.
Mr. Kenneth Anderson, Assoc. Director, National 4-H Service Committee.
Miss Emmie Nelson, National 4-H Service Committee.
Mr. John L. Strohm, Editor and World Traveler.
Mr. Everett Mitchell, Director of Agriculture, N. B. C., Chicago, Illinois.
Dr. Kenneth McFarland, Lecturer, Topeka.
Mr. D. Howard Doane, Chairman of the Board of Trustees, Missouri 4-H Foundation.
Mr. Clark Ellzey, Stephens College.
Dean Martha Biehle, Stephens College.
Mrs. Jessie Burrall Eubank, Stephens College.
Dr. W. A. Albrecht, Chairman, Department of Soils, University of Missouri.
Dr. Harry M. Philpot, Stephens College.
Dr. Wm. H. Alexander, Pastor, First Christian Church, Oklahoma City, Oklahoma.
Mrs. James D. Wyker, National President of United Church Women.
Dr. Evelyn Mills Duval, Author-Lecturer, Chicago, Illinois.
Dr. Russ Mawby, Assistant Director, 4-H, Michigan State University.
Miss Dorothy Emerson, Consultant, National 4-H Foundation.
Chase Irvin, Lecturer, Cape Kennedy, Florida.
Marilyn Van Derbur, former Miss America from Colorado.

Since 1959, the afternoon programs of 4-H Club Week have been workshops in health, wildlife conservation, music, safety, grooming, and courtesies. Delegates are enrolled in advance and take part in the workshop of their selection throughout the week.

Evening programs include mixers, parties, share-the-fun numbers, IFYE programs, and a candle lighting ceremony.

The campaign and election of State Council Officers have injected enthusiasm into the week's activities. The citizenship ceremony is participated in by 20 or more each year. This ceremony is a graduation for old members into full citizenship with voting privileges, and is for many the final 4-H participation as members.

Facilities were limited for the first few club weeks. Barracks in the veterans project provided housing for boys.

Barracks or University of Missouri temporary housing was provided for girls from the first year, 1946, through 1953. Since 1954, both boys and girls have been housed in University dormitories. Brewer Field House and the livestock pavilion, were used originally for assemblies. Since 1955, assemblies have been held in Jesse Hall Auditorium.

State Club Week saw improvements each year of its history. Today it is considered the outstanding state 4-H event of the year.

Some 399 members attended the first Club Week in 1946. Ninety-three counties participated that year. By 1964, the attendance figure had doubled, and the number of counties participating had increased to 105. In many cases unavoidable conflicts with other events have accounted for less than 100 percent attendance.

State 4-H Club Council

The Missouri State 4-H Council is the democratic representative of all 4-H club members in the administration of this youth program in the state. The Council is composed of four officers and fourteen district representatives.

Council officers are elected by State 4-H Club Week Conference delegates. A girl and a boy are elected from each of the Extension districts. All Council members serve for one year.

The Club Week campaign is a highly interesting event with two "political parties," the Greens and the Whites, presenting a full slate of candidates. Those interested in seeking office announce their intentions by filing the first day of the conference. Precincts are set up on dormitories floors where delegates are housed.

Polling places, judges, clerks, and secret ballots follow the pattern of a regular election. Different colored ballots are provided in different districts. This makes it possible for all delegates to vote for officers and for district delegates to vote for district representatives.

A major role played by the Council is planning and supervising the annual State Club Week program. Officers preside at sessions and various responsibilities are assigned to Council members. Matters given attention are in no way limited to Club Week. Many innovations have been made in the program as a result of Council action. The Missouri 4-H Foundation made provisions in 1964 for a monetary grant to provide funds for mailing of Council material to its membership.

The State Council was started during the first State Club Week in 1946. Three officers were elected. Herbert Clizer, Andrew County, was the first president. He presided at the sessions of the 1947 conference.

The first 4-H Council constitution specified that district representatives be elected for two-year terms and staggered the voting so that there would be a 50 percent carry-over, year after year. This didn't work very well in practice, and the constitution was changed in 1950, providing for convention-wide elections of four offices for one year only. In 1955, district candidates' names were placed on the ballot.

The theme of the 1951 club week was "Citizenship Challenges Youth," and featured the election. Lester O. Akers, state club agent, is credited with doing much in setting up and following through on the early elections. These political campaigns between the campaigners of the green and white parties provided grass roots experience in citizenship.

The first opportunity the State 4-H Council had for spending time on matters of its own came in 1955 when all Council members were made delegates to the Junior Leadership State Conference. Not only was the trip thus made economically feasible but allowance was made in the program for ample time for discussion of problems and proposals of Council matters.

Council meetings at the state level or at one of the Junior Leader Conferences were continued through the year 1963. Since that time the councils have matured to the point that they operate on their own and schedule two meetings a year which are held in Columbia.

Key Award Program

The Missouri Key Award Program was established in 1957. City Service Oil Company was the donor. The award is a specially designed key, and the program is especially for older 4-H club Members.

To be eligible to receive a key the member must be 16 years of age, and must have completed a minimum of five years of 4-H club work. The member must have a minimum of 100 points based on merits outlined in the Missouri 4-H Key Award Brochure.

		Keys Merited		
Year	Boys	Girls	Total	Counties
1957	70	156	226	85
1958	86	161	247	93
1959	101	153	254	96
1960	94	160	254	95
1961	106	148	254	96
1962	94	199	293	105
1963	95	190	285	96
1964	105	167	272	102
TOTALS	751	1,334	2,058	

The donor sponsors a banquet during State 4-H Club Week each year at which the awards are made. This program is a continuous one.

State Achievement Day

Community, county, district, and state achievement days follow a pattern. A member must be properly enrolled in a project or activity in order to enter a given event. Foods project members, for example, are eligible to enter demonstrations and judging contests and exhibit classes in foods. Grooming contestants must be members of a club that has selected that subject as a 4-H activity. There is no restriction on participating in a share-the-fun number since recreation is for all members of all clubs. Public speaking entries are enrolled in the junior leadership project.

Those participating in national events have gone, step by step, from community to county to district to state to national competition. Many members in meat animal, dairy, clothing, poultry, vegetable, and junior leadership programs have gone to national events.

Junior Farmers' Week

Junior Farmers' Week was a forerunner of the State 4-H Round-Up. It was conducted first as a section of the Missouri Farmers' Week Program in January, 1915. Attendance at Junior Farmers' Week in 1916 was 150, representing six counties.

The meeting time of Junior Farmers' Week was changed from January to May in 1923. It was held as a joint program for both club members and high school students in vocational agriculture.

In 1924, the program had considerable variety. It consisted of canning and clothing club exhibits along with a tour of the University grounds, College Farm, and Experiment Station.

Demonstrations by staff of the College of Agriculture and the Department of Home Economics were a part of the program, as well as judging contests in clothing, canning, livestock, and grain club projects. A picnic and a night program given by the Cosmopolitan Club of the University of Missouri were special features.

Due to the large attendance at Farmers' Week in Columbia, it was difficult to find lodging places for club members. It was also hard to keep the members grouped for contests and for other events which were arranged for them. It was decided not to increase the number of boys and girls at Farmers' Week, but to hold a number of club fairs.

Some 59 club fairs were held from October, 1915, to March, 1916, with 2,341 members present with 977 exhibits. Classes included poultry, corn, sewing, baking, canning, potatoes, pigs, and calves.

In 1925, the Junior Farmers' Week Program was divided into a 4-H club and a vocational agriculture section. Both were kept under the direction of one general committee, with the state club agent in charge.

In 1927, the budget, which had been appropriated solely to the 4-H Club Department at the Missouri State Fair, was divided equally by the State Fair Board between club and vocational agriculture departments. This reduction in funds necessitated a curtailment of the 4-H club program at the Fair.

Two changes in organization were made to meet this emergency: (1) The 4-H club section of the Junior Farmers' Week, previously held in April or May, was moved to August in 1928 and named the State 4-H Club Round-Up; (2) Only 4-H exhibits remained in the 4-H Club Department at the State Fair.

The nature of club contests and winners in those days is interestingly shown in the following excerpts from reports of 1915:

1. Best jar tomatoes, grown and canned by members. Silver cup donated by Mermod, Jaccard and King to Nellie Shelton, Holden, Missouri.

2. Second best jar tomatoes, same conditions. Set of knives and forks, given by Shapleigh Hardware Company, St. Louis, to Golda Moberly, Barnard.

3. Best written story of 200 words on the subject: "How I Canned My Tomatoes," Carberry Canner, donated by West Manufacturing Company, Philadelphia, to Margaret Hames, Tarkio.

4. Second best story of 200 words on the subject: "How I Canned My Tomatoes," two awards, each a pair of scissors, to Delta Deal, Holden, and Opay Snyder, Barnard.

5. For the best jar of tomatoes grown and canned by members, best written story of 200 words on the subject: "How I Grew My Tomatoes," best written story of 200 words on the subject: "How I Canned My Tomatoes," a trophy cup donated by the Missouri Bankers Association to Mary Turnbow, Pittsville.

Thirty-six buttons were sent to members who grew and canned tomatoes and submitted two stories of 200 words each, on "How I Grew My Tomatoes," and "How I Canned My Tomatoes."[73]

Second State Junior Farmers' Week

The second State Junior Farmers' Week was held in Columbia, January 4-7, 1916. Five ribbons were awarded winners in the following contests: Judging aprons, one acre corn production, judging beef cattle, making biscuits, judging bread, making button holes, judging corn, stringing corn for seed, judging canned products, ciphering match, judging draft horses, judging dairy cattle, making fudge, judging hogs, judging poultry, making patches, judging sheep, spelling match, darning stockings, club work, and attendance contest.

Boone County was represented with 43 contestants, Jackson 42, Buchanan 19, Marion 10, Pettis 8, and Cooper 8, for a total of 130.

Special awards at that second State Round-Up included: State shield, sweepstakes, awarded to Jackson County; stock judging, awarded to Marion County; corn judging to Jackson County; and home economics, also to Jackson County.

There were six formative years between 1914 and 1920. Projects were shaping up, standards were being established, requirements and literature written, and report forms made available to members.

Many Projects fell into place quite naturally. This was true for corn, pigs, and canning but other projects called for considerable effort to get comprehensive treatments of subject matter that would be practical and appealing to the young club members. Clothing and machinery, for example, at first appeared to be impossible to adapt to the club program.

World War I and the slogan: "Food Will Win the War" had its impact in greatly increased interest in club projects. Member enrollments in garden projects, for instance, increased rapidly to figures never since attained. Here was a mass movement with a minimum of organization, or teaching, and correspondingly low completion figures.

There is no doubt that worthy purposes were served, and it was apparent to the early Extension youth workers that a patriotic call to grow food to win the war would not be a lasting objective. Much building was required at the war's end to put what we now know as 4-H work on a solid foundation.

It will be noted that the basic ingredients of 4-H work—judging, demonstrating, and exhibiting—were included in 4-H work from its beginning. Club work officially started in 1914 and the first Junior Farmers' Week started in 1915. These ingredients have continued to be basic to the present day program.

Missouri State Fair

For more than four decades, 4-H clubs have had a prominent place at the Missouri State Fair at Sedalia. Exhibitions of Missouri 4-H work have been on a wide basis with all areas of the state represented. Certain events have on several occasions been centered at the State Fair.

Exhibits, other than livestock, poultry and vegetables, are housed in one of the largest buildings on the fair grounds. Four-H clothing, foods, home management, home grounds, woodwork, and electricity have been featured displays in the State Fair 4-H Building for many years. Collections of mounted insects, leaves, wood, and fruit of forest trees have had a place in the exhibits ever since entomology and forestry have been included in the 4-H manual. In recent years, photography has been a popular exhibit.

At the State Fair's livestock pavilion, an entire day is required to show a full classification of 4-H dairy cattle. The 4-H baby beef show has been an outstanding fair attraction since 1928. As many as 50 exhibitors have shown several times in a single class. In recent years, the number of animals in baby beef classes has decreased. There has been considerable increase in beef breeding classes since 1954.

In 1928, a junior activities department was created, which provided for county groups of five steers, 4-H or FFA, or combination of the two. This tended to stimulate beef entries. It assured county group entries enough premium money to pay transportation cost from the home county to the State Fair grounds.

Hogs have never played a prominent part in State Fair 4-H exhibits. In the 1920's some very creditable showings of hogs were made. Most of the exhibits were from Pettis County, however. Interest waned after that to where there were no 4-H swine exhibits at the Fair. One year the quality of those exhibited was so low that the judge, Professor L. A. Weaver, head of the animal husbandry department at the University of Missouri, refused to award a single ribbon.

There has been a gradual improvement in the quality and quantity of the 4-H swine entries during recent years to the extent that a barrow sale was held at the hog barn on the fair grounds. Some outstanding classes of barrows were exhibited. Some very creditable 4-H Club sheep have been shown, but entries have been light.

Prior to World War I, classes were offered in horses and mule colts shown "at the halter." Pioneer workers recall a few very good colt classes. The popular new 4-H horsemanship project has not yet had State Fair recognition.

Beginning in 1940, opportunity was provided for booth displays in the State Fair Building. Every booth had a theme pertaining to 4-H projects, activities, or general 4-H promotion.

Activities such as health, safety, and wildlife conservation were included in the booth displays that brought favorable comment for originality, resourcefulness, and educational value. IFYE displays have often been used. All competitive booth displays for cash awards were discontinued after 1963.

For 11 years (from 1953 through 1963) the state tractor skilled operators contest was held on the State Fair grounds. Since 1957 the final contests for this competition have been staged in front of the Grandstand preceding the Friday evening State Fair Show. This event was not included in the State Fair Premium Catalog as it was a state 4-H event conducted at the State Fair.

What had formerly been called the University of Missouri Building became known as the State 4-H Fair Building following World War II. The present building has been used for 4-H club exhibits and demonstrations since 1958. A feature of this building is its air-conditioned electric theater. Air-conditioning was installed in

1959. Here 4-H demonstrations are presented to State Fair visitors. They find this a very comfortable place to rest and view some very practical demonstrations.

Four-H exhibits and activities at the Missouri State Fair began in a modest way. In 1918, the first fair catalog that included what is now 4-H was published. Appropriations for the work amounted to $355.55. There were no facilities.

The first premium list showed the following premium list for club exhibitors:

Class	1st	2nd	3rd	4th	5th
Sewing courses	$10.00	$5.00	$3.00	$2.00	$1.00
Baking bread (2 loaves)	"	"	"	"	"
Canning one dozen jars-					
6 fruit, 6 vegetables	"	"	"	"	"
Corn - 10 ears	"	"	"	"	"
Poultry - cockeral &					
2 pullets	"	"	"	"	"
Pig - one	"	"	"	"	"
Calf - one	"	"	"	"	"
Sheep - at least two	"	"	"	"	"
Garden exhibit	$ 5.00	$3.00	$2.50	$2.00	$1.00
Stock judging contest	"				
Draft horses	$ 2.00				
Mules	"				
Beef cattle	"				
Dairy cattle	"				
Sheep	"				
Swine	"				
Sweepstakes	$10.00	$5.00	$3.00	$2.00	$1.00

This has grown to sixteen lots, 312 classes, and 5,411 exhibits. A partial list of the number of entries in 1963 was:

Clothing	1,563	Beef cattle	216
Foods	1,086	Swine	152
Home management	780	Sheep	159
Home grounds	231	Electricity	116
Dairy cattle	96	Woodwork	437

The amount appropriated for premiums in 1963 was $10,820. The department has been known by the following names:

1918-1924	Boys' and Girls' Club Work
1925-1927	Boys' and Girls' 4-H Club Work
1928-1929	Boys' and Girls' 4-H Department
1930-1937	4-H Club Department
1938-1951	4-H Division of Junior Activities Department
1952-1964	4-H Department

There were few 4-H facilities provided in the early years of the Missouri State Fair. Home economics 4-H exhibits were shifted from place to place as a limited amount of space was assigned to them from time to time. Agricultural exhibits fared little better and were housed with the respective open class departments.

The first space allotted to 4-H clubs at the Missouri State Fair was the former combined sheep and swine building at the northwest corner of Main and Wood Streets on the grounds. A whitewashed board wall room about 40' x 24' in size was provided for 4-H demonstrations and other member activities. The open class hog and sheep pens were vacated when the new $50,000 hog building was built on the west side of the grounds. Four-H swine and sheep exhibits were housed in the old pens. By the early 1940's, the University of Missouri Building was being shared with 4-H clubs and this continued until after World War II, when the University Building became the 4-H Building. Then in 1959, the Missouri Building was made the 4-H Building. This building has twice the capacity of the former University Building.

4-H Round-Up

What is offically known as the First State 4-H Club Round-Up was held on the campus of the University of Missouri in August, 1928. The event was continued with only a few changes for 14 years. The program started with registration on Monday afternoon and ended with a 4-H candle lighting ceremony on Thursday night.

The program replaced Junior Farmers' Week and certain events that had previously been held at the State Fair. Member participation included team demonstrations, team judging, health contests and girls dress revue. A county chorus singing contest was included some years.

Many adult 4-H leaders attended these round-ups. Member participation was limited to top individuals or teams selected at county round-ups which were later called county achievement days.

Evening programs consisted largely of recognitions, entertainment features, and recreation. The number of individuals and counties participating continually increased.

The last 4-H Club Round-Up was held in 1941 and was attended by 1,089 members from 89 counties. That year a state-wide 4-H Club Leaders Conference was held in conjunction with 4-H Round-Up, with an attendance of 75 leaders and prospective leaders. R. A. Turner, field agent, U. S. Department of Agriculture, led the leader discussions. The round-up programs were planned to meet the needs of both members and leaders.

Opportunity to live and work for a few days under university conditions was an inspiration to all who attended, adults as well as boys and girls.

Participation in contests developed a higher type of sportsmanship and better methods of carrying out farm and home practices.

Group discussions developed leadership abilities and gave all club members an opportunity to take part in thinking out club problems and of learning new ways of doing things in their home communities. The social, musical, and recreational activities added interest and gave balance to the program.

All members took part in daily group discussions on leadership. Of the total group in 1929, some 100 girls demonstrated 50 approved home practices, and 69 boys and girls gave team demonstrations of approved farm practices. A total of 44 girls took part in the clothing and food judging contests, 33 boys were in livestock judging contests, and 18 boys and girls were in dairy judging contests. A total of 18 club members took part in the corn judging contest.

An additional 15 boys and girls were in the leadership contests, 30 boys and girls from 22 counties entered the health contests, while 17 girls from as many counties participated in the dress revue.

Five counties had representatives in the singing and song writing contests.

In 1931, the 4-H delegates were provided with trips to the round-up. All, or part, of their expenses were paid by County Farm Bureaus, chambers of commerce, 4-H clubs, counties, banks, community organizations, women's clubs, by relatives, and by themselves. All members were required to be 12 years of age or older.

In 1932, the C. B. & Q. Railroad Company awarded trips to 32 outstanding leaders from counties served by that railroad. A feature of the week was the Annual State Conference of 4-H Leaders. Miss Gertrude L. Warren, representing the U. S. Department of Agriculture, led the discussions.

Top teams in all subject matter sections were eligible to participate in demonstration contests. Outstanding agricultural teams were named grand champions in agriculture. R. A. Turner, 4-H specialist representing the Federal Extension Service, served as judge of agricultural demonstrations for many years.

In 1936 a musical drama was presented as a new feature at the evening program on the University of Missouri campus south of Waters and Lefevre Halls. Groups combined to show seven periods in American life.

The program had been previously given at the National Club Congress and was adapted to the Missouri 4-H club program by Jane Hinote of the state 4-H club office, and directed by Jessalee Mallaliew, home demonstration agent. Ruth Muhleman and Glen Pittinger, county staff members, contributed much to the drama's success.

The attendance in 1941 of 1,085 members and leaders representing 89 counties of Missouri broke all-time records. An increase was noted in the number of members taking part in all events.

The University of Missouri provided the facilities for holding the state-wide 4-H Club Round-Up. In every way, 4-H club work was recognized as an important responsibility of the University of Missouri's College of Agriculture.

The morning general assemblies of the Round-Up were held in the auditorium of Waters Hall from 1928 through 1939. The evening sessions were also held in this auditorium until 1933 when the attendance had so increased that it became necessary to have an open-air assembly at night.

The evening meetings were then held near the east end of Jesse Hall on the University of Missouri campus, using a temporary stage. The evening meetings were held there for a few years. In 1938 and 1939 the evening programs were held in the baseball grandstand on Rollins Field. All of the general programs, both morning and night, in 1940 and 1941 were held in Brewer Field House because there were no other facilities on the campus capable of accommodating the 1,000 or more spectators.

The club girls and leaders attending 4-H Club Round-Up were housed in private homes, Read Hall, women's gymnasium, and Stephens College dormitories from 1938 through 1940. In 1941 the girls lived in private rooms and Gentry Dormitory. The boys were first housed in private homes and then had temporary housing at Rothwell Gymnasium from 1931 to 1941.

In 1913, all 4-H Club members ate at the University of Missouri Cafeteria. The women of the Missouri Methodist Church in Columbia served 4-H Club members meals in the church dining room from 1934 through 1940.

Some of the activities in 1941, the last year of 4-H Club Round-Up, included talent night by county groups, also the dress revue and the "well groomed boys and girls contest."

The awarding of two University scholarships on Wildlife Conservation Achievements by Edward K. Love Wildlife Conservation Foundation; two scholarships on dairy achievements by the St. Louis Dairy Products Corporation and the Chapman Dairy Company of Kansas City; and the concluding candle lighting ceremony were important events of each year's concluding program.

4-H Short Course at Lincoln University

A short course for Negro 4-H club members from several southeast Missouri counties served by Negro agents, was held in 1947 at Lincoln University, Jefferson City. Delegates from nine counties took part. Pemiscot, Dunklin, Mississippi, New Madrid, and Butler Counties were the main participants.

A total of 178 members and leaders attended the first meeting. Since that time other county delegations have been included. Lincoln University has always been the host. Delegations were housed in the University's dormitories and dined at the cafeteria.

Dr. J. N. Freeman, Head of Lincoln University's Agriculture Department, was the originator, mainstay, and manager of this event for 19 years. More than 3,000 young people shared this experience.

The program was planned on the order of the 4-H State Club Week held on the University of Missouri campus. It began on Tuesday afternoon and was concluded on Thursday night. On Friday the group visited places of interest in St. Louis such as the zoo, attended a Cardinal baseball game, and visited Shaw's Garden. An afternoon during the week was devoted to a tour of the State Capitol in Jefferson City.

The program was terminated in 1964 when Missouri 4-H programs became totally integrated. Delegates that formerly would have gone to the Lincoln Short Course now attend State 4-H Club Week at the University of Missouri.

On the national level the Regional 4-H Conference for Southern states was terminated in 1961 and the first Negro delegates began to attend the National Conference at Washington, D. C., in 1963. Missouri had a Negro boy in the 1965 delegation.

4-H Turkey Show

The 4-H Turkey project has developed much interest in a select number of Missouri communities. State and national turkey shows have contributed to the success of this program in Missouri. The first state turkey show for 4-H members was held in 1956. It was sponsored by the Missouri Turkey Federation. It was a junior show for both 4-H and FFA members. Contestants entered with 100 poults. Deanne Borron of Sullivan County showed the grand champion dressed bird. It weighed 27 pounds.

Deanne also showed the reserve champion bird—another 27 pounder— in 1957 at the National Turkey Show in Chicago.

State Junior Leader Camp Conferences

The special focus on junior leadership in camp conferences during the five-year period, 1954 through 1958, has paid good dividends in terms of the junior leadership project and the entire 4-H program. A summary of participation during the period follows:

Year	Jr. Leader Camp Conf.	Health Camp Conf.	Conservation Camp Conf.	Health Clinic
1954	147	89	87	
1955	175	91	82	
1956	149	98	63	
1957	146	82	77	115 (K. C.)
1958	161		87	180 (Columbia)
Totals:	778	360	376	295

All were held at the Clover Point Camp in Lake Ozark State Park. All were sponsored by the Missouri Electrification Association. Julius Helm was executive manager of the association.

Nothing so well illustrated growth in the scope of 4-H club work as a comparison of the early state camp programs and the junior leadership programs at Junior Leaders Conference.

The main speaker for all five conferences was Prof. Clark Ellzey of the marriage and family department at Stephens College. Each year a series of four one-hour lectures by Prof. Ellzey, one each night of the five conferences, was enthusiastically received. Personality development and needs of teenagers were the topics discussed. Prof. Ellzey was available for individual counseling throughout the program.

Speech was emphasized each year. Mrs. Helen Williams of Columbia's Hickman High School faculty trained the delegates in speech the first year. Mrs. Fred Krusekopf of Columbia did the same the next two years, Miss Patricia Elliott of Springfield, Missouri, the fourth year, followed by Mrs. Krueskopf the fifth year.

All delegates prepared and delivered short talks to working groups and selected members to speak to the entire assembly. The six work periods were devoted to selecting a theme for a talk, choosing subject, organizing material, and making presentation.

Special interest sessions were devoted to leading indoor recreation, outdoor recreation, presiding, discussion, dramatics, photography, and news. Mrs. Marian Beebe, of the state 4-H staff, directed a special session at the 1957 camp on the subject of "appearance." A professional hairdresser was featured on the programs and demonstrated methods of that art.

John Kadlec, University of Missouri assistant football coach, had charge of the afternoon programs that included waterfront activities, archery, and other skills. Lester O. Akers, a member of the state 4-H club staff, and a former Seabee, conducted a course in water safety at all the state camps during the five years of the camp's existence.

Square dancing after the Ellzey lectures and one boat ride on the Lake of the Ozarks completed the evening programs.

After 1958, five district junior leader camps replaced the state camp and are still being held.

District Junior Leader Camp Conferences

Junior Leader District Camp Conferences following the pattern set at the state camps have continued to the present time, with participation as follows:

	Year	Junior Leaders Attending
2	1956	309
3	1957	232
6	1958	403
5	1959	600
5	1960	518
5	1961	552
5	1962	524
5	1963	396
5	1964	460

Totals: 3,994

It stimulated participation in National 4-H Citizenship Short Courses, which have been attended by more delegates from Missouri than from any other state.

The Conservation Camp

The first State Conservation Camp in Missouri was held at Montauk State Park in October, 1935. Some 60 4-H club members attended. The Federal Cartridge Corporation, Minneapolis, Minnesota, provided $500 to pay board and lodging of campers for three days. Charles L. Horn was, and is, the president of that corporation.

Back in the thirties, George W. McCollough, wildlife technician, for the Federal Cartridge Company, had the concept of a conservation camp in every state in the Union to interest youth in conservation. This was in the depression days when survival was of more concern than conservation.

Nevertheless, Mr. McCollough attempted to sell the idea of sponsorship to the Association of Ammunition Manufacturers. The idea met with favor, but not enough favor to cause these sponsors to adopt the plan. Mr. Horn was so thoroughly sold on the idea that he said, "To heck with you fellows. I'll take it on myself." He did, or his corporation did, and provided $500, then later $600, and finally $700 to sponsor a conservation camp for Missouri 4-H. Apparently no other youth organization was considered in the plan.

Mr. Horn, who has given this project a prominent place in his very busy life, was one of the first two "Friends of 4-H" to be so honored. R. V. Duncan of St. Joseph, Missouri, and Mr. Horn were honored by the Missouri 4-H Foundation at the State 4-H Club Week in 1953. It is interesting to note that Mr. Horn and Mr. Duncan were the sponsors of the joint Health and Conservation Camps for many years. Mr. McCollough attended and contributed to the programs of most of the camps.

A camp was held every year from 1935 through 1957. Most camps were held at state parks—Montauk near Salem; Bob White at Knobnoster; Hawthorne and Pin Oak at Lake of the Ozarks; and finally at Clover Point, also in The Lake of the Ozarks State Park, which became its home. An abandoned CCC Camp was rehabilitated by the Park Board in 1949 primarily for 4-H. It was officially named Clover Point in honor of club work's four-leaf clover emblem.

The Missouri Conservation Commission came into being in 1936. Since then members of the Conservation staff, now known as the Missouri Department of Conservation; members of the staff of the Cooperative Wildlife Service of the University of Missouri; Extension specialists in forestry, entomology, agricultural engineering, and others, have provided technical talent for the conservation camp programs.

Among those who were household names in delegate families in the early years of the service were: Dr. Rudolph Bennett, Charles Swartz, Lisle Jeffrey, Harold Terrell, Kenneth Hicks, Olin Capps, Cecil Davis, and many Field Service men. From 1935 to 1938 the University of Missouri College of Agriculture primarily provided the resource people and among them were Prof. Leonard Haseman of the entomology department and Prof. H. H. Krusekopf of the soils department.

Early programs were largely informational, dealing with soil, animal and plant life. Soon though, the camp programs were planned to implement "action programs" for water, food, and shelter for wildlife.

In 1947, conservation camp delegates were selected from 4-H members showing junior leadership qualities with a special interest in conservation. This was continued until 1958 when the last camp was held. The chairmen of conservation activity standing committees returned to their respective clubs with new ideas and inspiration after attending a conservation camp.

Many miles of multiflora rose were planted by 4-H members. This plant provides protective cover for quail and has food value. Hence, if near water, all three essentials of food, cover, and water are met. Hundreds of members were trained in gun safety, angling, and pelting. Ponds were stocked with fish.

In the early days of the camps a tradition was started of dividing campers into the Fin, Fur, and Feather Tribes. In general, these campers learned their conservation lessons well.

The Health Camp

The first 4-H Club Health Camp in Missouri was held in 1947 and was repeated for 11 years. It was held in conjunction with the Conservation Camps. Kellogg Company of Battle Creek, Michigan, provided the camp funds from 1949 through 1952.

R. V. Duncan of the Iowa-Missouri Walnut Company of St. Joseph, Missouri, became the sponsor in 1953 and three important changes were made: (1) The number of delegates increased more than threefold. Twenty-five had been the standard number. In 1953 it was 87 delegates. (2) Separate programs were adopted for conservation and health. "Happy, Hearty, and Healthy" units parallelled the Fin, Fur, and Feathers units of conservation. (3) The camp delegation was to be composed of chairmen of the health standing committees of local clubs.

State Department of Health staff, Extension specialists and physical education staff members of the University of Missouri provided the technical help from the beginning.

The program became a junior leader program devoted to health. The junior leaders chose the health phase for their project, or were chairmen of health committees.

Programs were directed toward water safety, highway safety, immunization against rabies, physical check-ups, good lighting, good nutrition, good posture, prevention of communicable diseases, health habits, physical fitness, and many others.

Methods used included discussions, visuals, check sheets, talks, illustrated talks, demonstrations, drama, surveys, and reports.

Two conferences, called Health clinics, sponsored by the Folgers Coffee Company in 1957 and 1958, were held in Kansas City and Columbia, and were designed especially for health committee chairmen.

District Events

District 4-H Achievement Day

District 4-H Round-Ups came as a World War II emergency measure in 1942, replacing the State Round-Up that had met with favor during the years 1928-1941. It was presumed at the time of the change that this plan would only be a temporary arrangement and that the state event would be resumed after the war emergency.

The District 4-H Round-Ups met with such favor that they have been continued to the present time. Then too, participation increased so rapidly after World War II that the state event would have soon become unwieldy without the district events which filled in very logically between county and state events.

The District Round-Ups followed the pattern of the State Round-Up, but were one day instead of five. Most of the changes introduced during the war years were prompted by "the stress of the times."

In the very beginning, in 1942, the district program occupied a full day and evening. It was concluded with presentation of awards, entertainment, and a candle lighting ceremony.

In the second year, 1943, the number of district events was increased from 12 to 17 to further reduce travel. Club presidents, or others representing the presidents, were added to the delegation and group discussions were added to the day's schedule.

Members who gave talks on 4-H activities and general club problems had prominent places on the programs in the 1944 round-ups. In 1945, evening programs were discontinued. A recognition service was held for former 4-H members who were at that time in military service. This service had a special place on the afternoon program of the 1945 round-up.

A polio epidemic interrupted the 4-H program in 1946. This made necessary some postponements. After 1947 the district programs were expanded, and district 4-H round-ups and district achievement days continued some of the new features which had been added, such as share-the-fun in 1952, public speaking in 1954, and several judging contests. Through the years the number of district contests has been reduced.

Nearly one-half of the counties of the state have served as host counties to district round-ups during the period 1942 to 1964.

The name of the event, District Round-Up, was changed to District Achievement Day in 1955. It was a change in name only, and not in program.

In 1942, some 2,200 4-H members participated in district achievement days. Some 22 years later, or in 1964, a total of 2,911 4-H members took part.

Between 1922 and 1964, a total of 42 years, demonstrations, dress revue, and grooming have been a part of the district programs. The health contest was a carry over and continued in the program until 1947. Public speaking was added in 1954.

In the early 1940's all 4-H judging contests were included. After state appropriations for district 4-H fairs were introduced in 1943, judging contests were gradually shifted to district fairs. In 1961, judging contests were again included in round-up programs.

There has been an increase worthy of notice in public speaking. There were 55 participants in 1954; 77 in 1955, and 118 in 1963.

Sixty-five counties participated in share-the-fun district round-ups the first year in 1952, and some 200 members participated each year thereafter, until 1958 when the figure increased to 640 and gradually increased to 878 in 1963.

Negro agents, leaders and members have held their own achievement days. In 1963 eight representatives from the Lilbourn Achievement Day for Negroes participated in the State Achievement Day.

It was announced that beginning in 1965 the only contests included in the State Achievement Day will be those in which delegates are selected for national contests.

District Fairs

Fairs . . . fairs . . . fairs. We have lots of them in Missouri open to 4-H entries. Mention is made in the "teen years" of a campaign for encouraging local, county, and district fairs. Now no county, district or state fair is complete without a 4-H section. There is the Ozark Empire fair at Springfield with a full classification for members in a large area of Missouri.

Club members in northwest counties have participated in the Aksarben (Nebraska spelled backwards) 4-H Livestock Show in Omaha.

Diagonally across the state to southeast Missouri, Delta counties have been included in the 4-H division of the Mid-South Fair at Memphis, Tennessee.

The Joplin Market has been host to 4-H livestock shows and sales from four states — Missouri, Kansas, Oklahoma, and Arkansas dating back to the 1930's.

However, 4-H district fairs have a special meaning. These date back to 1943 when "Hoot" Elijah, livestock specialist for the State Department of Agriculture, started a movement for establishing five 4-H district fairs with state appropriations from the State Legislature. This was a war measure but the practice was continued.

Mexico, Cape Girardeau, St. Joseph, Sedalia, Rolla, West Plains, Warrensburg, Springfield, and others have shared in the state appropriations for 4-H district fairs. Livestock and dairy judging contests, for instance, consistently sent only teams from these fairs to state achievement days where state teams have been selected for national contests.

St. Jospeh Young Cattlemen's Show and Sale

One of the most challenging 4-H livestock projects is called the "young cattlemen's." It represents a departure from the usual baby beef show.

Animals are fed in lots of five or multiples of five starting in the fall and marketed the following December.

Objective is to produce beef that will grade good to choice with a minimum of 25 bushels of corn or grain equivalent.

The show and sale is conducted in the stockyards. Consignments are judged on management and finish of the steers.

Those meriting blue ribbons are taken on a bus trip to livestock farm feeding operations.

4-H Club Camps

"It was 4-H camp time. The camp was held at Moberly where suitable facilities were available. Charlie Kyd, Randolph County agent, had made arrangements. He was camp manager but all of us shared in the work. There were probably 100 club members there.[34]

"Harold Slusher, Callaway County agent, had brought with him two girls from St. Louis who were spending the summer at the farm home of their godmother in Callaway County.

"One of the girls was small and quick and took part in everything; the other, about 13, had grown rapidly and felt awkward. As a result she had developed the habit of staying in the background.

"We divided into groups for easy direction. The older girl was in my group. Let's call her 'Rose' which was not her name. As we started our first game we formed a circle with everyone joining hands. Rose backed over to the wall. Beside me there was one older girl—a natural leader. As we passed Rose each took her by the hand and she became a part of the circle. From then on she felt like one of the group.

"It was the last morning of camp and we were getting ready to go home. I had called my group together to tell them how much I had enjoyed being their leader. I felt a hand slip under my arm. It was Rose. Then she said: 'Mr. King, can't we play just one more game?' I told her to start the record she wanted played.

" 'I'll never forget this camp', she said in parting. I doubt if she ever will. I had seen a wallflower blossom into a beautiful Rose."

Organized and guided camping became part of the Missouri Boys and Girls Club program in the early 1920's. The first period of 4-H camp development in Missouri is that decade between 1923 and 1932.

The first club camp in Missouri was conducted at Blanchett Park, near the city of St. Charles, in 1923. The camp idea was an instant success. In 1924, the club members of 12 counties attended six camps of some three days each, with a total

---

[34] From a letter from Raymond T. King, Marshall, Missouri; in the files of the University of Missouri Extension Service, Columbia.

enrollment of 910 persons, including 176 boys, 328 girls, and 408 local leaders, agents, sponsors, and friends.

The main objectives of 4-H camping were: (a) To teach camping; (b) to enable the campers to enjoy themselves, and, (c) to encourage the members, leaders, and other participants to assume camp responsibility.

The early camps often were housed in large tents, usually provided by the State Cooperative Extension Service and by the Missouri State Highway Department. Sometimes the campers were billeted in rustic cabins at vacation resorts, in public parks, or on picnic grounds.

The location of early camps was determined mainly by the availability of sleeping quarters, swimming facilities, suitable playgrounds, and ample shade. Later as the camps became more permanent, they were set up preferably in isolated areas, in wooded parks, away from the "beaten paths" of villages and towns.

Sleeping quarters varied. There was the crude method of "bedding-down" the boys and men on loose straw in one large tent or hall, and putting the girls and women in another, but similar place, each camper with bedding from home. Some quarters offered more privacy and comfort, and each camper slept on an army cot or in a cabin bunk.

Meals usually were paid for from the small fee collected from each camper or club. The food often was supplemented with some brought from homes, and occasionally by donations from local commercial and civic clubs. In a few early camps, the meals were served cafeteria style, out-of-doors under the trees which became difficult on rainy days; but most often, the meals were served in a large tent or hall which often was used for recreational and program purposes.

In 1924, practical club problems were considered. These included: Camp duties, getting-up exercises, and flag-raising ceremonies.

Contests in conducting typical club meetings, giving method demonstrations, judging club products, health clinics, and group games also were important on camp programs, as were leaders' planning conferences, tours to scenic places, nature hikes, and trips to industrial plants or stores. Night campfire programs were conducted, including stunts, friendly visiting, and moving pictures, with many parents and friends present at the last evening in camp.

A representative camp council system of self-government was begun in 1927. A group discussion by the members and leaders had become a feature of most camps. A camp newspaper had been added. And practically all camp programs were being concluded on the last night in camp with a public candle lighting ceremony.

As a general thing, each camp had the services of a nurse. Swimming permits, signed by the parents or guardians, were required of each camper who planned to swim or take swimming lessons.

Handicraft was added to the club programs in 1928 and forestry tours in 1932. In the meantime, supervised recreation had become a part of most camp programs.

After some 10 years of consistent camp growth, 4-H camping in Missouri came to retrenchment about 1932. The years, 1932-1938, often referred to as the depression years, are known as the second period of 4-H camping in Missouri.

This 1932-1938 period of camp decline ended by reestablishment of more favorable conditions, approximately at the end of 1938 or beginning of 1939. In 1933, the number of 4-H camps dropped in Missouri from 12 to six and the total camp attendance form 1,148 to 589. In 1938 there were 33 camps conducted with a total attendance of 3,537 persons from 91 counties, consisting of 1,219 boys, 2,000 girls, and 318 adults.

During this period of camp changes, instead of holding regular three-day camps, many counties substituted over-night, or all-day camps and evening picnics. This conserved time and money, but lowered camp standards. Adjustments in camp programs included greater emphasis on nature study and science.

In 1938 training schools were conducted for agents before the camping season, so they could assume larger responsibilities later on in camp.

Tensions brought about by the depression years of "the thirties" were reduced somewhat through the application of practical social studies. These were planned to make it easier for people to live together in camp and at home. Consideration was given to "everyday courtesies" and "personality needs."

During the years 1938 to 1942, camp enthusiasm waned. This was the third period of camp activity in Missouri.

In 1940, there were 34 camps conducted in Missouri with a total attendance of 3,440 persons from 103 counties, including 1,194 boys, 1,788 girls, and 458 others.

By 1943, the total camp enrollment in Missouri had dropped to 2,270 persons representing 70 counties, and including 681 boys, 1,034 girls, and 495 others. This reduced interest in club camping continued through 1944.

In 1945, the total enrollment in camp was 6,888 persons, representing 100 counties, consisting of 2,206 boys, 2,855 girls, and 1,827 adults.

As during the hard times of the depression years of the 1930's, many all-day picnics were conducted, beginning with breakfast and closing with a night Missouri 4-H candle lighting ceremony. Short over-night camps were often held as a substitute for the former three-day camps.

In 1940, it was noted in the survey of Extension workers, at both the county and state levels of leadership, that there were 1,874 camp members who were under 15 years of age; another 1,566 were 15 years of age or older. This age situation suggested the possibility of dividing the large camps into two sections with the programs adapted to interests of members at different age levels.

The responsibility for conducting the Missouri 4-H camps for several years had shifted slowly from the state club staff to the county agents and home agents. County agents had been trained in state camp conferences prior to the camping season of June, July, and August.

However, the state staff continued to serve as specialists in 4-H camp activities on the same basis which subject matter Extension specialists have with the county agents and county home agents.

In 1946 demonstration camping areas that had been developed by the Interior Department were given over to the Missouri State Park Board. Included were three units in Cuivre River State Park, two units in Knobnoster State Park, and four units in Lake Ozark State Park. Four of these units were made available to

Foreign IFYE delegates to the U.S. are pictured at a mid-point meeting on the University of Missouri-Columbia campus in 1960.

Van Eitel
Belgium—1949

Scott Sawyer
France—1950

John Gerber
Switzerland—1952

Maribel Mor
England—195

Helen McHugh
Germany—1954

JoAnn Noble
Scotland—1954

Patricia Redhage
Chile—1954

Shirley Yag
Finalnd—195

Jack Melton
Greece—1956

Dorothea Drane
Denmark—1957

Rodney Garnett
Norway—1957

Mary Johann
Luxembourg—1

Robert Knoernschild
Japan—1959

Edmund Bohl, Jr.
Australia—1960

Glenda Rhoads
Sweden—1960

Rebecca Willi
Argentina—19

MISSOURI INTERNATIONAL FARM YOUTH EXCHANGE

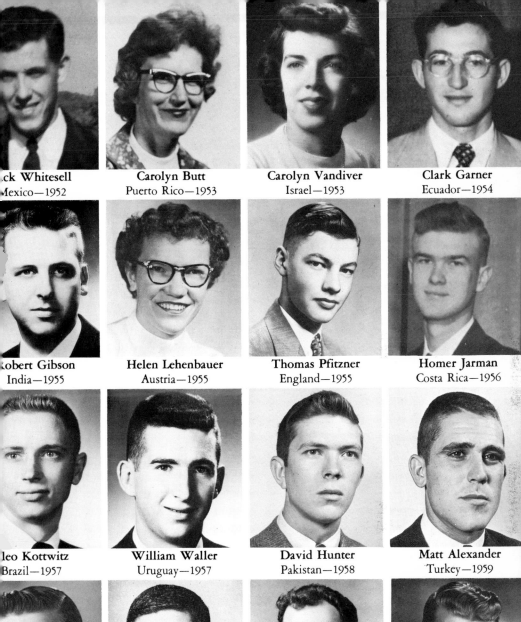

ck Whitesell
Mexico—1952

Carolyn Butt
Puerto Rico—1953

Carolyn Vandiver
Israel—1953

Clark Garner
Ecuador—1954

obert Gibson
India—1955

Helen Lehenbauer
Austria—1955

Thomas Pfitzner
England—1955

Homer Jarman
Costa Rica—1956

leo Kottwitz
Brazil—1957

William Waller
Uruguay—1957

David Hunter
Pakistan—1958

Matt Alexander
Turkey—1959

LeRoy Huff
Ireland—1963

John Crouch
Venezuela—1964

Robert Ferguson
Peru—1964

Robert Horton
New Zealand—1954

DELEGATES HAVE GONE TO 32 FOREIGN COUNTRIES

(See Appendix for complete list of IFYE delegates)

*Heiner Kiefaber, IFYE
delegate from Germany, lived
with the Virgil Goff family
in Worth County in 1952.*

*Glenda Rhoads of Pettis County, a 1960 delegate to Sweden, is shown interviewing
the 1961 outbound Missouri IFYE delegates. The outbound delegates are: Marjorie
Faeth, St. Clair County; Nancy Ewing, Vernon County; Tom Risch, Franklin
County; Anna Lou Karrasch, Andrew County; Byron Rosbrugh, St. Clair County.
See appendix for lists of outbound and inbound delegates and host families.*

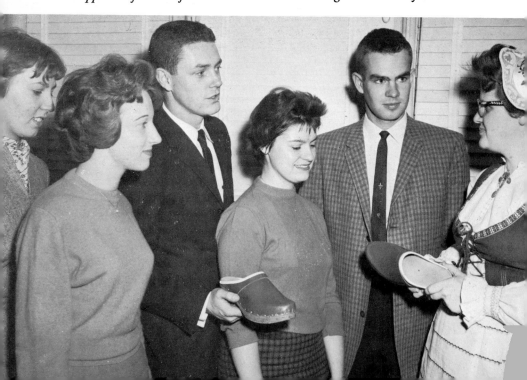

At right is the Missouri delegation to the First National 4-H Club Camp in 1927; T. T. Martin, state leader; Roy Nicholson, Ray County; Albert Dyer, DeKalb; Nellie Jones, Buchanan; Elsie Gibson; Caldwell; Jane Hinote. The picture above, in 1935, gives a view of the setting for early camps north of U. S. Department of Agriculture Building.

President Herbert Hoover greeted the third National 4-H Camp in 1929. Missouri delegate, Lola Acklin, Nodaway County, stands second from the left. Mrs. Hoover (below) presented awards.

Clark Griffith, owner of the Washington Senators and former Missourian, requested that the Missouri delegation to the 1941 Club Conference be photographed at Griffith Stadium. Reuben Brigham, Extension editor; Jack McFarron, Jasper; Marceline Langford, Newton; Clark Griffith and Mary Lentz, Jackson; James Heitmeyer, Monroe; and Robert S. Clough.

Marjorie Nold, Andrew County, presented President Harry Truman with a 4-H Leader pin while attending the 1951 National 4-H Conference.

Byron Simpson, Missouri delegate, stands at left of President Eisenhower at 1957 National 4-H Club Conference.

Missouri delegates Steve Mills, Newton; Marsha Ann Nicholson, Shelby; Patricia Minks, Franklin, and Leon McIntyre, Nodaway; with Senator Stuart Symington (D-Mo.) at 1964 National 4-H Club Conference.

Missouri delegates to 1961 National 4-H Club Conference presented a podium made of Missouri walnut for the Missouri room at the National 4-H Center. Left to right are John Crouch, Jewel Fraunfetter, J. C. Sykes (National 4-H Foundation), Quinten Huss, Frank Graham, Patsy Mathew and Grant Shrum.

First delegation to National Club Congress to be photographed was this 1944 group.
First row: *Arthur Schneider, Cole County; Georgia Hannah, Nodaway; Herbert Clizer, Andrew; Loro Elizabeth Crowley, Andrew; Paul A. Clark, Andrew; and Rosalie Kilp, Saline.* Second row: *May Sontag, State 4-H Staff; S. D. Elliot, Mercer; Della Marie Koechig, Cape Girardeau; Walter Wilkening, Cape Girardeau; Shirley Habluetzel, Buchanan; Harvey Lee Musgrove, Scotland; Cleta Null, State 4-H Staff; and Robert S. Clough, State 4-H Staff.* Back row: *Shirley Corrough, Nodaway; John Hohm, Cole; Sue Broaddus, Randolph; Keith Smith, Johnson; Elizabeth Tomlin, Linn; Jack Clark, Henry; Frances Ann Halferty, Clay; Robert Schrock, Cass; and Dolores Burroughs, Nodaway.*

This 1953 delegation included the following. First row: *Kathy Poirot, Dade County; Bob Heitmeier, Monroe; Okle Conover, Lewis; Johnny Giddens, Buchanan; Marie Kirchdoerfer, Cape Girardeau; Don McCool, Clinton; Evelyn Taylor, Lewis; and John C. Fallert, Ste. Genevieve.* Second row: *Jean Randolph, Andrew; Kathleen Greenwell, Monroe; Phyllis Brown, Cass; Mollie Lou Osburn, Dunklin; Patricia Redhage, Franklin; Norma Homfeld, Lafayette; Phyllis Vogelsmeier, Saline; Gerald Lubbering, Cole; and Pat Coppersmith, Nodaway.* Third row: *Norma Mossman, Buchanan; Russell Rosenbohm, Nodaway; Howard Brooks, Audrain; Ben Joe Summers, Howell; Vincent Hulshof, New Madrid; James Norman, Lawrence; Robert Rice, Barton; and Mary Barman, Nodaway.* Fourth Row: *Robert S. Clough, Vance, Henry, Ruth Upchurch, state club agents; James Hughes, Cedar; Jeaniece Haubold, New Madrid; and Keith Boyer, Scotland; Charline Lindsay and Grant Shrum, state staff, and Cordell Tindall, Missouri Ruralist, Fayette.*

Lincoln University, at Jefferson City, was host to Negro 4-H delegations from 1948 to 1965. Pictured is the 1950 delegation. Dr. J. R. Freeman, head of the agriculture department at Lincoln University, was manager of the short courses. He is shown at the extreme upper left.

The 1960 regional 4-H Club camp delegates visit with Vice-President Nixon in Washington, D. C. Left to right: W. C. Cooper, 4-H leader, N.C.; Robert Jones, Bridgeville, Dela.; Marilyn Wilder, Freemont, N.C.; Mable Jones, Malden, Mo.; William Johnson, Greenville, Ala.; and Vice President Richard M. Nixon.

Howard Harvey and Thomas Cooper, Hayti; Elmore Nelson, Jr., Caruthersville; and George Harris, Charleston, attend 1962 4-H Short Course.

Missouri delegates to the Fourth Regional Negro 4-H Camp, Pine Bluff, Ark., in 1951 were, l. to r., David Humes, Pemiscot County; Murphy D. Miles, Mississippi; Guida Joyce Jackson, Scott; and Joe Reeves, Stoddard.

Delegates to the Fifth Regional Negro 4-H Camp, Tuskegee, Ala., in 1952 were Johnny McWilliams, Jr., New Madrid County; Annie Irene Higgins, Pemiscot ;Mattye Marie Berry, New Madrid County home agent; Mildred Hawkins, Dunklin County; and George Wesley, Jr., Pemiscot County.

Members of the Rocheport 4-H Club in Boone County view some of their beautification work with Jeanette Palmer, Extension home economist.

Clay County 4-H Club members taking part in a 4-H Sunday (1950s).

First row: Nancy Lambert, Linn; Virginia Stonner, Saline; Rebecca Hargus, Atchison; Robbie Faye Flowers, New Madrid; Shirley Metcalf, Franklin; Pearl Clemons, Cunklin; Zeta Combs, Gentry; Brenda Bier, Marion. **Second row:** Beuhal Nichols, home economist; Bill Barry; George Brown, Greene; Jack Simmons, Dade; George McIntyre, Nodaway; Dale Alumbaugh, Lafayette; Dewayne Powell, Jackson; Billy Correll, Linn; Mrs. Sue Gerard, national alumni winner, Boone. **Third row:** Jeannette Palmer, home economist; Lynn Hitchings, Iron; Sandra Postlewait, Atchison; Joyce Fortner, Clinton; Janice Clark; Jackson; Donna Bailey, Jackson; Carolyn Sue Noyes, Barton; Lola Barnett, Christian; Charline Lindsay, Extension youth specialist. **Fourth row:** Fowler Young, extension district director; James Hodgson, agricultural editor; Doug Fortner, Clinton; Milton Cone, Johnson; Jack Forrest, Randolph; Robert Jackson, Adair; Jimmy Newson, Chariton; Spencer Miller, Jackson; Frank Graham, Extension youth specialist. **Fifth row:** Don Bailey, youth agent; Jack Kinnett, Laclede; Phillip Hanson, Pike; Terry Hedeman, Dade; James Devier, Boone; James McMillan, Dallas; O. C. Swackhamer, national alumni winner, Atchison; Arthur C. Ausherman, Extension youth specialist.

National winners from Missouri at the 1963 4-H Club Congress in Chicago included both members and adults. Here, Frank Graham, left, state 4-H agent, is pictured with Rebecca Hargus, Tarkio, $500 scholarship winner in canning program; Phillip Hanson, Bowling Green, scholarship winner in health; and Mrs. Sue Gerard, Columbia, and O. C. Swackhammer, Tarkio, national alumni winners.

Both 1956 national achievement winners were from Missouri. They were Robert Teegarden, Caldwell County, and Jo Ann Warshburn, Linn County.

Attending 1957 Junior Fact Finding Conference, l. to r., are Connie Foote, Gerry Luebbering, Karen McIntyre, John Burkeholder, Margaret Cottrell, Bill Collie, and Dorothy Breedlove.

Pictured here, looking at a replica of the Chicago Board of Trade trading floor are, from left; Ronnie Shepherd, state 4-H grain marketing winner; Henry M. Wolf, second vice-chairman, Chicago Board of Trade; Gifford Boswell, assistant county agent, Cassville; and Charles Grathwohl, state 4-H grain marketing winner.

Missouri 4-H delegation at the 1962 Junior Fact Finding Conference. Sitting, l. to r.: Jack Forest, Randolph County; Leon McIntyre, Nodaway. Standing: John Burkeholder, state staff; Glen Geiger, poultry specialist; Linda Alkire, Buchanan; and Jack Kinnett, Laclede.

Seated, l. to r., at 1962 4-H Dairy Conference are Joyce Fortner, Clinton County; Allen Smith, Vernon. Standing: Clem Koenig, Clinton County Youth Agent; James McMillan, Dallas County; Robert Miller, Barry; and Dale Allenbaugh, Lafayette.

Elmer Ellis, president of the University of Missouri, strolls with President Truman, speaker at the 1957 State Club Week in Columbia.

State 4-H Council officers John Crouch, Clay County; Quinten Huss, Clinton; and Bonnie Shirley, Chariton; visit Governor John Dalton. (1961)

Byron Simpson of Clinton County makes a safety talk. (1955)

The 1964 State 4-H Council. First row, l. to r.: Chuck Humphreys, president; Cathie Wiehe, secretary; Ralph Gates, vice-president; Carmen Pope, treasurer. Second row: Steve Smith, northeast; Linda Hawkins, northwest; Cindy Meyers, east central; Peg Hepworth, northeast, Kathy Frank, south central; Susan Krone, west central; Dorothy Farrer. Third row: Brian Novak, east central; Sam Swan, southeast; Jack Simmons, southwest; Terry Lister, south central; Cheryl Hedeman, southwest; Eddie Grotjan, northwest.

4-H campers. All of these had facilities complete with dining hall, cabins, and swimming, and some had recreation halls.

The State Park Board then rehabilitated an abandoned CCA Camp that gave a preference to 4-H groups. The expanded camping program included good facilities in Roaring River, Pershing, Mark Twain, and other State Parks.

In 1948 interested citizens from 13 southeast Missouri counties provided a complete camp at Wappapello Park. Hence 4-H camping facilities that were improvised at the start are now equipped for modern camping in every section of Missouri.

County Events

4-H County Achievement Day

No where in America will be found a youth activity comparable to the County Achievement Day. One day is set aside, usually in July or August, for every county in the State of Missouri.

The uniqueness of this event lies in the nature of the day's program. The content is determined by the projects and activities that have been chosen by members of the different clubs. Every county is different. All may include judging, demonstrating, exhibiting, and dress revue for clothing project girls, a grooming contest for boys and one for girls, a public speaking contest for junior leaders, and share-the-fun acts.

Many county achievement day programs will include all of these. The group system of evaluating all contests is used. Entries are rated blue, red, white, or no ribbon. The top blue ribbon participants are eligible to move on to a district achievement day where they will compete with winners from other counties of the district.

Some but not all county participants are selected at club achievement day—usually a regular club meeting—and held in advance of the county achievement day. Regulations will determine participation in the county event when no local achievement day is observed.

Parents and friends of the contestants provide the audience for those interested in the various programs. Members not performing learn from one another as they observe the events during the day. A final assembly of all participants closes the day's program with the awarding of ribbons.

Many times the program is extended into the evening and is concluded with a beautiful candle lighting ceremony.

County Fairs

Club fairs are held in many counties. The premium list usually covers all exhibits produced by members. Provisions are made for 4-H exhibits in all Missouri counties having county fairs.

4-H Club Sunday

The broad outline of this history is built around projects, activities, events, and motivating forces. A special Sunday for 4-H, or 4-H Sunday doesn't fall in any of these categories and yet this narration would be imcomplete if some mention of it is not made. It fits into the Heart "H" that best typifies the "Spirit of 4-H." A single observance of 4-H Sunday once a year should not be considered in itself adequate consideration of the heart symbolism. Four-H members and leaders range from the devout to the indifferent. One worship service a year and occasional vesper services do not give religion a prominent place in the 4-H program. The 4-H program does recognize that religion needs a place in character building programs for youth, but it leaves religious training to church and Sunday School and encourages participation in these activities.

It is well known that the spirit of fair play, helpfulness, leadership, and adherence to high ideals is woven into the very fabric of the entire 4-H program.

A Sunday dedicated to 4-H is not one of national observance. Traditionally, "Rural Life Sunday" is and has been recognized as 4-H Sunday. The 4-H club organization no longer is thought of as strictly rural, but the tradition does hold.

The earliest Christian observance of what is today called "Rural Life Sunday" began in the late fifth century in the city of Vienne in Gual. Vienne had been the victim of severe earthquakes, fires, and other calamities, and its bishop ordered the people to join in solemn fast and prayers beseeching God for deliverance.

The consequent observance of three days of prayer spread throughout the church and was enlarged to include prayers for "the appeasement of God's anger at man's transgressions, to ask protection in calamities, and to obtain a good harvest." They came to be called Rogation Days from the Latin *rogare,* to beseech.

In 1929, at the suggestion of the International Associatin of Agriculture Missions, Rural Life Sunday was first proposed as an interdenominational celebration in the United States. It was recognized by the Home Missions Council of North America and the Federal Council of Churches of Christ in America, both now incorporated in the National Council of the Churches of Christ in the U.S.A.

The special day reserved for its celebration is the fifth Sunday after Easter, or the last Sunday in April if the fifth Sunday conflicts with Mother's Day. Four-H club observance of Rural Life Sunday is called 4-H Sunday.

In Missouri, 4-H Sunday was first observed on July 12, 1936. Nine counties sponsored the first 4-H Sunday services that year.

Those counties were: Cass, Carter, Reynolds, Chariton, Daviess, Dent, Gasconade, Lewis, and Shelby.

In 1961, a quarter of a century later, 4-H Club Sunday was well established in Missouri. There were 4-H Sunday services in most of the 114 counties of the state. Approximately 25,000 members of 4-H Clubs attended, or participated, in the services.

The Missouri School of Religion in Columbia has traditionally provided resource people from its faculty for program materials. Ministers throughout the state have been very cooperative in their support of 4-H Sunday.

Recognition Night

Many counties observe a recognition night at the close of the club year. This is a time for summaries and reports, and for recognizing voluntary adult leaders. It is also a time for distribution of pins to those who have merited credit for satisfactory completion of a year of 4-H club work. Recreation always has a prominent place in the recognition night program.

Other County Events

Picnics, square dancing, skating, hay rides, county softball leagues, and various athletic and other events are planned and conducted at the county level in the 4-H club program.

Many counties conduct regular meetings including recreational activities with the County Junior Leader Council.

Club Events

Many community 4-H clubs have the size, maturity, and resourcefulness to plan club events similar to the way county 4-H events are planned and carried out. This closes the chapter on 4-H events with the hope that we leave the reader with the feeling that the 4-H organization offers opportunity for achievement, adventure, creativity, and leadership, as well as service to and by the 4-H members of our beloved Missouri.

Chapter VII

RESOURCE AGENCIES—THE STRONG RIGHT ARMS OF 4-H

Missouri 4-H Foundation . . . Demonstration Youth Centers . . .
4-H Banker Builders . . . Missouri Land-Grant College . . .
Missouri Cooperative Extension Service . . .
Federal Extension Service . . . National 4-H Foundation . . .
National Service Committee . . .

Missouri 4-H Foundation

The Missouri 4-H Foundation was organized in 1949 and is composed of men and women interested in furthering the good work of the 4-H club program. The Foundation is composed of a Board of Trustees and an advisory committee.

Main objectives of the Foundation is 4-H work beyond the support given it by the Federal Extension Service and the University of Missouri. To this end, special emphasis has been given to the recognition and training of voluntary 4-H leaders.

Counsel, guidance, and some financial support are given by the Foundation for establishing youth centers. These provide facilities for making plans and programs for character building youth organizations in Missouri.

The Missouri 4-H Foundation has set up a trust fund with Boatmen's National Bank of St. Louis, the earnings of which are to be used by the 4-H program where it will do the most good. The assets of the fund now are about $250,000.

D. Howard Doane of Point Lookout, Missouri, was chairman of the Foundation's first Board of Trustees. Others who have served in this capacity for two or more years are: Don K. Spalding, St. Joseph; E. G. Cherbonnier, St. Louis; John Sam Williamson, Columbia; Ray Miller, Osage Beach; and Olen Monsees, Jefferson City.

Program of the 4-H Foundation

The major projects during the 15 years of the Foundation's existence (1949-1964) have been:

1. Recognition and training of voluntary 4-H Leaders . . . sponsored community leader camp conferences . . . radio recognition.

2. Recognition of "Friends of 4-H."

3. Radio quiz programs with 4-H members to inform the public and to publicize 4-H.

4. Demonstration youth centers.

5. Memorial trust fund, earnings of which are to be used currently.

6. State Bankers Building Program—annual joint solicitations for the Missouri 4-H Foundation and National 4-H Foundation.

Friends of 4-H Plaques Presented by the Foundation

The Board of Trustees of the 4-H Club Foundation began in 1953, a practice of honoring two friends of 4-H each year by presenting Citation Plaques.

Those honored are private citizens, not connected with Federal or State Extension Services. Plaques are presented during the State 4-H Club Week. The following have been cited for outstanding service to Missouri 4-H club work:

1953 R. V. Duncan, President, Iowa-Missouri Walnut Co., St. Joseph
Charles L. Horn, President, Federal Cartridge Co., Minneapolis, Minn.

1954 A. W. Godfrey, Manager, Robertson's Inc., St. Louis.
Gene Wetherell, Extension Rural Minister, Missouri School of Religion, Columbia.

1955 C. B. Denman, Farm Leader, member of Federal Farm Board, Farmington.
Harry Wright, Manager, Livestock Producers Association, St. Louis.

1956 A. F. Stephens, Agricultural Agent, G.M.&O. Railroad, St. Louis.
Harry Garlock, Vice-President, St. Joseph Stockyards Co., St. Joseph.

1957 A. J. Renner, Milling Company Executive, Sikeston.
Robert E. L. Hill, Executive Manager of Missouri Bankers Association, Columbia.

1958 Les Harper, Sturgeon State Bank, Sturgeon. State Chairman for many years of Bankers' Builders Committee of the National 4-H Foundation.

1959 E. L. Dale, Carthage *Evening Press,* Carthage.

1960 J. W. Reid, Robertson's Inc., East St. Louis, Illinois.
Cordell Tindall, Editor, Missouri Ruralist, Fayette

1961 Richard C. Green, President, Missouri Public Service Company.
E. J. Gildehaus, Director, Farm and Rural Service, Union Electric Company, St. Louis.
Mrs. William E. West, 4-H Benefactor, Kansas City.

1962 L. Reed Holt, KFAL Radio, Fulton.
Donald Danforth, Ralston Purina Company, St. Louis.

1963 Mr. John Bennett, President, United Stockyards Corp., Chicago, Ill., (Residence—St. Joseph, Missouri).
Mr. Kenneth Hicks, Field Service Coordinator, Missouri Department of Conservation, Jefferson City.

1964 Joe Welman, President, Bank of Kennett, Kennett, State Chairman of Bankers' Builders Committee of the National 4-H Foundation.

D. E. Wimberly, Rural Safety Director, Arkansas-Missouri Power Company, Blytheville, Arkansas.

Missouri 4-H Foundation Loan Fund

The Board of Trustees of the Missouri 4-H Foundation placed $4,000 with the University of Missouri's 4-H Foundation Loan Fund on November 2, 1961. This fund is directed by Allan Purdy, director of aids and awards for students at the University. Loans from this fund must be to former members of a 4-H club in Missouri, and preferably to students in their junior or senior years.

A gift of $3,000 was made by H. D. Wright, Manager of Producers Livestock Marketing Association, National Stockyards, Illinois, in 1961. It was the residue of a fund provided by the St. Louis Producers for the purchase of breeding ewes for 4-H project members during the 1940's and 1950's. The gift was made at the suggestion of E. S. Matteson, University of Missouri Extension animal husbandry specialist.

It was Matteson's fine counsel that made possible the success of the 4-H club sheep program, involving more than 20,000 project animals. The additional $1,000 was contributed from the 4-H Foundation treasury.

Demonstration Youth Centers

One of the most challenging projects the Missouri 4-H Foundation ever undertook was the establishing of demonstration youth centers in the state. The Board of Trustees offered $5,000 to any local group that would cooperate in setting up a youth center that would serve as a demonstration.

Such a demonstration was needed to provide a pattern for planning facilities that might serve the many purposes of various youth organizations, with special emphasis on 4-H, but open to all character building groups. The pattern involved the selecting of a site, incorporating, overall planning, financing and planning for detailed development of the area.

In the early stages of this project, a bulletin was published that detailed the "what" and the "how" procedure. This bulletin was made available to those interested, and a general invitation was extended to make application for the grant.

Near the end of 1964 a site was chosen for a center and plans completed for a demonstration in Clay County. The local cooperating group was the Clay County Agricultural Youth Center, Inc. Mrs. Earnest Shepherd of Liberty gave 40 acres about three miles north of Liberty on Highways 69 and 33, with a promise of 23 additional acres for the demonstration area.

Mrs. Shepherd's gift is a memorial to her husband. She, and the Clay County Board of Directors and the Foundation Youth Center Committee, took steps to safeguard the use of the property in order to fully perpetuate it for the purpose intended.

The launching of this enterprise meant the fulfillment of a dream for D. Howard Doane. Very early in his administration, as the first Chairman of the Foundation's Board of Trustees, he began sharing his ideas for fulfilling a need of the youth of Missouri with fellow members of the board. First mention appears in the minutes of the April, 1954, Board meeting. C. B. Denman moved that the trustees be interested in the movement, and be kept informed on the progress of the movement.

In September 1962, a donor committee was appointed to raise $5,000 as a beginning for setting up the demonstration center. This committee was composed of:

> *D. Howard Doane, Chairman, McCreadie*
> *Lyman Neel, Columbia*
> *Virgil Burk, Columbia*
> *T. A. Ewing, Springfield*
> *John Sam Williamson, Columbia*
> *E. G. Cherbonnier, St. Louis*
> *C. L. Harper, Sturgeon*

Members of this committee visited a number of prospective sites in Jackson, Saline, Clark, Marion, Boone, and other counties. The Clay County offer appeared to meet the standards for the first demonstration.

Miss Mary McGinnis Deeds Land for 4-H Youth Center

Late in 1964, word came to D. Howard Doane from E. S. Matteson that Miss Mary McGinnis and her brother, C. C. McGinnis, both of Rich Hill, were interested in making gifts of land for a 4-H demonstration youth center in southwest Missouri. Subsequently, Miss McGinnis deeded 160 acres for this purpose.

West Memorial 4-H Trust

A significant event in the celebration of the 50th Anniversary of the Extension Service was the establishment of the 4-H West Memorial Trust. In 1964 the Boatman's National Bank of St. Louis was named manager of a trust fund, the corpus of which will remain intact. Earnings will be used for worthwhile purposes in the 4-H program through the years.

The fund has now grown to almost $250,000. It will no doubt exceed that amount when the West Estate is liquidated.

William E. West was a successful businessman of Kansas City. He died in 1954 leaving his estate to his widow, Catherine E. West, with a request that the residue of her estate be left to youth organizations.

Mr. West was a native of Bolckow, in Andrew County, Missouri. He was a "self made man" who "started from scratch." Through wise business acumen he accumulated a small fortune in banking, loan associations, and investments.

It is not known whether he ever had direct contacts with 4-H members and leaders. No doubt he was familiar with the program. He did have an appreciation for self reliance, a basic ingredient of the 4-H club program. He included four youth organizations in his will, one of which was 4-H clubs.

After Mr. West's death, his widow came to know many 4-H members and leaders and made a number of $500 gifts to the Foundation during her lifetime. She was given a citation plaque as a "Friend of 4-H" during the State 4-H Club Week in 1961. She died in December, 1962. Her will provided, after certain personal bequests were made, that one-third of what was left of her estate should be given to the Missouri 4-H Foundation. Her plan provided funds for the West Memorial Trust. Mrs. West was born in Harrison County and spent many of her earlier years in Ripley County. She was known to all as a very gracious lady.

Late in 1964, President Olen Monsees of the Missouri Farm Bureau, appointed a committee to consider projects that would be financed by the earnings of the West Memorial 4-H Trust. It was in keeping with sentiments expressed by D. Howard Doane:

"We are now in sight of an income of $5,000 to $6,000 per year from the West Estate. The temptation to spend it on "spur of the moment" needs, projects, or urging of individuals or groups will be great.

"We want this income to go to work, do worthwhile things within the objectives of this Foundation. The surest way to make every dollar produce maximum dividends will be to consider a whole series of proposals by every member of the board. We should appoint a 'sifting' committee that will make selections and recommendations, then commit the funds in accordance with carefully considered programs, the kind that will yield maximum results".

The committee given the responsibility to make recommendations along the line of Mr. Doane's suggestion were:

> *James E. Stevens, Chairman, Kansas City*
> *Mrs. E. Y. Crouch, Liberty*
> *William Heimer, Taylor*
> *Karl Wickstrom, Springfield*
> *Robert S. Clough, Columbia*
> *Frank Graham, Ex Officio, Columbia*

Cherbonnier Bequest

Plans are in the making whereby E. G. Cherbonnier, a charter and still active member of the Foundation Board of Trustees, will deed to the Foundation property in Ferguson valued at some $15,000. This property will doubtless be liquidated and the proceeds deposited in the Boatman's National Bank Trust Fund, St. Louis.

The principal sums of the West and Cherbonnier thrusts will be kept intact. Earnings will be used appropriately as the donors wish.

Other Bequests and Gifts

Original planning by the leaders of the Missouri 4-H Foundation sought to make possible an organization which could accept various funds from people friendly to the whole 4-H program. They tried to make it easy for donors to contribute.

Founders of the Missouri 4-H Foundation and all successors on the Board of Trustees and the advisory committee have been keenly aware of their responsibility in safe-guarding funds entrusted to them.

In keeping with that high resolve, all services of 4-H Foundation Board members have been voluntary. None has received compensation for services or compensation for expenses incurred in behalf of the Foundation. And in 1962, members of the Board contributed a very large portion of the $5,000 for the first demonstration center.

First contribution of consequence to the 4-H Foundation was made by Ellen Chesley Caverno Barrett, Exceutrix of the estate of Louis Ray Caverno.

The contribution was in honor of Xenophin Caverno. Mr. Caverno was a resident of New Madrid County. He was one of the pioneers in agricultural Extension work, the Farm Bureau organization, and was the first chairman of the State Agricultural Adjustment Administration Committee. The contribution was for $1,000. Mr. Caverno died September 13, 1941. Mrs. Barrett's check was dated November 29, 1952.

C. B. Denman of Farmington, St. Francois County, died November 7, 1958. His will made a bequest to the Missouri 4-H Foundation that amounted to $795.91. C. B. or "Cy" as he was popularly known throughout the United States, called himself "a St. Francois county farmer." His sphere of influence, however, extended far beyond the confines of his community and county.

Mr. Denman was an impressive speaker. He became known throughout Missouri as an organizer for the Missouri Farm Bureau Federation. He was on the original Board of Directors of the Producers Livestock Marketing Association at the East St. Louis market.

Later he was a member of the Federal Farm Board, and was the first counsel for the National Foods Chains with an office in Washington, D. C. He was a charter member of the Board of Trustees of the Missouri 4-H Foundation, and vice-president for many years.

Mrs. Katherine Simmons of Rock Island, Illinois, made a bequest to the Foundation in her will, dated December 26, 1958. The bequest is designated as "Burns Memorial Scholarship Fund." It was made in memory of the grandparents of Mrs. Simmons, Jacob and Ester Burns, and her parents, John Edward and Edie Eliza Davis Burns, all of Scotland County, Missouri,

Mrs. Simmons is a native of Scotland County. She is still living. The bequest is for 80 acres of land in that county. The grandparents came from Ireland and settled on this land. The father was born on this farm. In her will, Mrs. Simmons states, "I wish to establish a living memorial."

4-H Banker Builders

Early in the life of the National 4-H Foundation, established in November, 1948, a "Banker Builders" program was started with Jesse W. Tapp, chairman of the Board of the Bank of America, representing the American Bankers Association, as president. Mr. Tapp appointed Joe Welman to solicit funds for the National 4-H Foundation. Mr. Welman is president of the Bank of Kennett. He was the first Missouri state chairman for the Builders' Committee.

In 1956, Grant R. Shrum, then executive secretary of the National 4-H Foundation, suggested that the Banker Builders program should be a cooperative program for the National and Missouri Foundations. As a result of that suggestion, Extension Director J. W. Burch named a committee to meet with Mr. Shrum to consider the matter.

The meeting was held at the Tiger Hotel in Columbia. Those present were: R. E. L. (Bob) Hill, Executive Manager of the Missouri Bankers Association; J. W. Burch; J. Rogers Cochran, Treasurer of the Missouri Foundation Board of Trustees; L. C. (Les) Harper, President of the Bank of Sturgeon; Robert S. Clough, Chairman, Missouri State 4-H Club Staff, and Mr. Shrum.

The committee agreed that the solicitation should be made jointly and the money shared by the two Foundations, and that Mr. Harper be asked to accept the responsibility of state chairman with Mr. Tapp's approval. This approval was readily given and Mr. Harper continued to serve from 1956 through 1962.

Final arrangements for the 1962 solicitation were made at the hospital by other trustees during Mr. Harper's fatal illness. He died in 1962. H. L. Harlin, president of the Bank of Gainnesville, was named state chairman in 1963.

The banks and the amounts they contributed were:

Year	Banks	Amount	Chairman
1956	112	$1,758	Harper
1957	101	$2,153	Harper
1958	125	$1,668	Harper
1959	143	$2,060	Harper
1960	181	$2,260	Harper
1961	132	$2,042	Harper
1962	134	$2,105	Harper
1963	181	$2,555	Harlin
1964	103	$1,790	Harlin

In recent years the major portion of money collected from banks has been applied to the costs of district junior leader conferences. The banks, taken collectively, may be considered co-sponsors, with the Sears-Roebuck Foundation, of the junior leader conference program.

Radio Quiz Programs

D. Howard Doane, the first chairman of the Board of Trustees of the Missouri 4-H Foundation, originated the idea for a unique kind of 4-H radio program which was sponsored by KFAL at Fulton.

Merchants in the central Missouri area sponsored the program for eight years, 1955-1963. L. Reed Holt was responsible for developing and keeping interest alive in this series. The program consisted of four members, from each of two clubs, in different counties being given questions in "spelling bee" fashion. Scores were given for correct answers, and a club winner was declared for each session.

Programs were set up on a series of seven, starting with eight clubs and eliminating until a top team for the series was determined. Sometimes top teams of two different series were pitted against each other. Several series were limited to age groups of 13 and under, and 14 and over. A total of seven counties participated in these broadcasts. Sets of questions for a given program were arranged in categories, such as: *organization, projects,* and *activities.* All phases of 4-H work were included.

The KFAL 4-H quiz program set the pattern. Under the direction of the agricultural editorial staff, additional programs were set up involving some of the counties of the state for the greater part of a year or less.

Among the stations taking part were: KMMO, Marshall, starting April 19, 1957; four counties, KHMO, Hannibal, March 16, 1957; seven counties, KCHI, Chillicothe, 1958; five counties, KIRK, Kirksville, April 13, 1958; four counties, KWPM, West Plains, 1959; KWRT, Boonsville, 1959; KWIN, Maysville, 1958.

National 4-H Foundation

The National 4-H Foundation has as its main function the securing of private funds to supplement the 4-H program, nation-wide. The Foundation is an incorporated body, governed by a 15-man Board of Trustees. On the Board are representatives of the Federal and State Extension Services and national 4-H sponsors. Mr. Frank Graham, Missouri's Youth Program Director, is a member of the Board.

The program of the Foundation is administered by a professional staff. It is headquartered in the National 4-H Center in Washington, D. C.

Norman Mindrum of Minnesota was the first director. He resigned in 1958 to become director of the National 4-H Service Committee. Grant A. Shrum, a native Missourian, and former member of the Missouri state 4-H club staff, became executive secretary of the Builder's Council, later known as the National 4-H Sponsors Council, on October 15, 1955. Shrum succeeded Mr. Mindrum, as director, May 16, 1958, and remains in that capacity.

The buildings and a 12½ acre campus at 1700 Connecticut in Chevy Chase, Maryland, were purchased by the Foundation in February, 1951, dedicated that year, and formally opened in 1959.

Missouri 4-H members contributed $3,000 to furnish a room in the main building of the Center, and this was officially named "The Missouri Room." It was dedicated by the 1961 delegation to National 4-H Conference, and bears the insignia, "Dedicated to the Ideals of 4-H."

Citizenship Short Courses

More than 3,000 members from every state and Puerto Rico took part in the 1964 citizenship programs at the National Center in Washington, D. C. A high percentage of these came to the Center as delegates to the National 4-H Citizenship Short Courses.

The first 4-H Citizenship Short Course was held in 1959. A single county, Buchanan County, Iowa, participated that year. A full week of programs at the Center, with tours and visits to national shrines comprised the program. A 10-week schedule for the summer months every year since 1959 has brought the total participation for the six years to 8,921 from 38 states.

Beginning in 1960, Missouri participation in this program has exceeded that of all other States, with a total of 1,298. One delegation from southwest Missouri attended in 1960. Seven delegations with 219 members attended in 1961. More than 300 Missouri 4-H members have attended every year since.

The three states with greatest participation in this program for the entire 1960-1964 period are: Missouri, 1,298; Michigan, 1,034; and Iowa, 946. No other state has exceeded 500. All Missouri delegates have been junior leaders.

National 4-H Leader's Forum

Seven hundred 4-H leaders from 32 States attended the 4-H Leader Forums in Washington, D. C. in 1964. Total participation since the program began is 1,890, with Ohio, Virginia, and Michigan leading.

The program consists of visits to historic shrines and important government offices along with classroom work. Study is concentrated on improved understanding of needs and capabilities of youth.

One Missouri leader attended this conference in 1961, four in 1962, and bus loads in 1963 and 1964. A total of 64 have participated. It appears that the practice of assembling a bus load of Missouri 4-H leaders every year for participation in this program has become established.

National 4-H Citizenship Laboratory

Ten states accepted an invitation to send 4-H club members to a special laboratory in citizenship education to be held at the National Center in Washington, D. C., in July, 1963. Each state was represented by a team of five including four members and one adult leader. An exception was made for Missouri.

Two teams were sent from this state, including one from Lincoln County. A team was sent from southeast Missouri which included Negro members and a leader. The two-weeks laboratory was conducted by the staff of the National Foundation under a grant from the Readers Digest Foundation.

Nine teams were chosen for the 1964 Citizenship Education Laboratory. The 1963 Missouri team members were:

Jamie Sue Harness, Charla Ann Howard, Gerald Shannon, Charles Wieman, and Gilmer Dehn, Extension youth agent from Lincoln County; John Cassell, Floyd Watson, Earlean Nicholson, Artie Ellison and William Purnell, Extension area agent for southeast Missouri counties.

Civic Leaders Institutes

The first Civic Leaders Institute was held in 1964 and was attended by young adults representing 13 states and the District of Columbia. They came from many groups, including Farm Bureau young people, Girl Scouts, Farmers Union, Grange, and other rural youth organizations.

Human Development Workshop

The 4-H Foundation and the Sears-Roebuck Foundation have continued their support of training for Extension personnel through sponsorship of the National Workshop in Human Development and Human Relations for the past 13 years.

Consultant Service

The citizenship and leadership resources of the 4-H Foundation are made available to 4-H members and leaders in many ways. One of the most popular 4-H Foundation resource persons is Miss Dorothy Emerson. She traveled in 30 states from Maine to Alaska during 1964 urging 4-H members and adults to adopt, "I'll be glad to," as a general philosophy.

Representing Missouri at the first 4-H Laboratory in Citizenship Education at the National 4-H Center, Washington, D. C., 1963, were, l. to r.: Jamie Harness, Middletown; John Cassell, Wolf Island; Charla Howard, Elsberry; Gilmer Dehn, Extension youth specialist, Troy; Floyd Watson, Sikeston; William Purnell, Extension area agricultural agent, Charleston; Gerald Shannon, Elsberry; Charles Wieman, Moscow Mills; Carlean Nicholson, Vanduser; and Artie Ellison, Charleston.

National Citizenship Short Course delegation from Audrain, Boone, Callaway, Cole, Moniteau, and Osage Counties in 1967.

Newly-selected 4-H Reporters-to-the-Nation for 1965 look over news copy being sent out from National 4-H Club Congress. Reporters from Missouri are: Melody Richardson, Brunswick (6th from left) and Charles Humphreys, Marshall (8th from left.)

Six 4-H Reporters-to-the-Nation with President Kennedy in March, 1961. Others in the picture are, Elmer Winner, Office of Information, U.S.D.A.; Bill Smith, Pennsylvania State; Charline Lindsay, state club agent from Missouri; Marguerite McNally and Christensen Clim, National Service Committee; Robert F. Quain, Conrad Hilton Hotel, host; Norman Mindrup, director of Service Committee; Mrs. Quain; Ed Aiton, Federal Extension Service; Frank Welch, Assistant Secretary of Agriculture; Orville L. Freeman, Secretary of Agriculture; Milo Downey, Federal Extension Service.

Southwest Missouri delegation to 1962 National 4-H Citizenship Short Course in Washington, D. C. Congressman Durward G. Hall is at the extreme right.

First bus load from Missouri to the third National 4-H Leaders Forum, 1965.

A bequest of Mr. and Mrs. William E. West of Kansas City, Mo. in 1964 provided the Corpus of a more than $250,000 trust fund that will be of invaluable service to this and future generations of Missouri 4-H members.

Members of the first Board of Trustees of the Missouri 4-H Foundation established in 1949. Left to right, seated: C. B. Denman; D. Howard Doane, president; and James W. Burch, Extension director, who appointed the board. Standing: Robert S. Clough, state club agent; Pete Renner; Frank Graham; J. Ed Rutter; and Don K. Spaulding.

R. V. Duncan, Iowa-Missouri Walnut Co. owner, is shown receiving a "Friends of 4-H Plaque" from Sara Coad at the 1953 State 4-H Club Week. Another plaque went to Charles Horn, president of the Federal Cartridge Co. Others in the picture are James Burch, George McCollough, Robert Clough, Don Spaulding, and D. Howard Doane.

The seventh annual meeting of the Missouri 4-H Foundation's Board of Trustees in September, 1956, was attended by left to right, standing: Wendell Holman; E. M. Copeland, Jackson County leader; John Sam Williamson; Olen Monsees; Robert S. Clough; C. L. Harper; Frank Graham; James W. Burch; L. Reed Holt. Seated: D. Howard Doane; E. C. Adams, Sr.; E. G. Cherbonnier; Don K. Spaulding; J. R. Cochran; Pete Renner.

At the mike at 1957 KMOX leader recognition party in Franklin County is Ted Manger. Mrs. Bruns, adult leader, right; Paul Schoene, county youth agent, standing; and Mrs. Marian Beebe, state 4-H agent, left, assisted three junior leaders with interviews.

Shown in the upper picture are Mrs. Earnest Shepherd, left, who gave the land; Robert Lincoln, chairman of the Youth Center's grounds committee; and Mrs. E. Y. Crouch, member of the Missouri 4-H Foundation board. Below is a broader view of the shelter and show ring. The Center also includes a lighted baseball diamond and camp grounds used by Scout groups.

National 4-H Center, 7100 Connecticut Ave., Washington, D.C.

Peace Corps Projects

The National Foundation has contracts with the Peace Corps to operate in Brazil and Uruguay. About 135 volunteers served Peace Corps projects in 1964.

The Brazil 4-H project started in 1962 and the project in Uruguay began in 1963. A 5-V project in Venezuela was completed in April, 1964, and the 4-H Foundation took over a continuing 4-H project in Sarawak in July of that year.

The National 4-H Service Committee

In 1919, Guy L. Noble, a member of Armour and Company's Bureau of Agricultural Economics, became interested in giving more rural boys and girls a chance to attend the International Livestock Exhibition in Chicago. He persuaded his company to provide $5,000 to sponsor 40 all-expense trips to Chicago for the 1919 Livestock Show.

When the International Exposition time rolled around, Noble found himself surrounded not only by the Armour delegation but by about 100 boys and girls who were in Chicago as guests of their local communities, businessmen, railroads, and other sponsors.[35] Noble cheerfully included all of them in the tours and entertainment planned. This was the beginning of what is now the National 4-H Club Congress, known to every 4-H club member as "The Time of Your Life" event.

In May, 1920, Mr. Noble arranged for a leave of absence from Armour and Company. By July of that year he had become so enamoured of his work that he resigned his Armour job to devote full time to the new work he had created.

In 1920 the sponsored delegations numbered 500; in 1921 they numbered 675. It was Guy Noble who suggested to men interested in the movement that there should be a committee to oversee the total program.

Such a committee was formed and announcement of its personnel was made to the 675 members of the 1921 meeting in Chicago. They included:

E. T. Meredith, Des Moines, publisher of Successful Farming, and former Secretary of Agriculture, Chairman; Guy L. Noble, Secretary; members—John Simpson, J. W. Coverdale, F. L. Eaton, B. H. Heide, E. M. Hopkins, O. M. Plummer, R. M. Striplin, Thomas E. Wilson, George E. Farrell, and R. F. Eagle.

Thomas E. Wilson, founder of Wilson and Company, became chairman in 1924 and because of his interest and good work was prevailed upon to continue in that position until 1958.

In 1923, Montgomery-Ward appropriated $5,000 of which $4,000 was to be used for educational trips, and the balance to cover committee expenses. This developed into the Girls' Record Award, a continuous program. It is now called the Home Economics Award Program.

---

[35]Clyde H. Duncan, author of this book, along with four other club boys and State Club Agent W. J. Jernigan, represented Arkansas at that first national gathering in 1919 in Chicago, later to become the National 4-H Club Congress.

The name "Club Congress" was used for the first time in 1923. The program of the National Committee grew until the staff occupied two floors of a downtown Chicago office building, with its own service company, its own magazine, and a budget of $1,775,786 in 1964. Guy Noble continued as director of the committee until his retirement in 1957.

The National 4-H Service Committee's work has been expanded greatly with the passing of time. The program of sponsored trips to Club Congress, national scholarships, training programs, and various other awards and services remains the hub. The name of the committee was changed to National Service Committee in 1960.

National Awards Programs Sponsors[36]

Sponsors of the 4-H National Awards Programs provide for county, state, and national awards. These include medals for county winners, all-expense trips to the National 4-H Club Congress for state winners, and scholarships for national winners.

The Montgomery-Ward 4-H sponsorship set the pattern in 1919. The number of sponsors grew gradually through the years until by 1964 some 23 Club Congress trips were offered on a state basis, two others on a sectional basis, and three on a national basis.

The amounts of national scholarships have grown from $200 to $500. Some National 4-H Club Congress trips are offered at the state and sectional level. The number in the Missouri delegation varies slightly from year to year. Missouri's quota for 1964 was 32 members.

The National 4-H Club Congress is held each year, beginning on the Saturday after Thanksgiving, and concluding the following Thursday night.

A valuable sponsorship of educational awards is provided by the Atchison, Topeka and Santa Fe Railway System. This is limited to Missouri and surrounding states. Five educational Club Congress trips and two $500 scholarships for current or former Santa Fe delegates were provided in 1964. The support provided by this railroad has continued for 42 years.

Additional educational trip awards include those given by the Chicago, Burlington and Quincy Railroad Company for $225. This railroad has been a sponsor for 38 years.

Eight delegates are selected for a U. S.-Canadian 4-H Exchange sponsored by International Minerals and Chemical Corporation, Skokie, Illinois.

The six national awards scholarship winners in the health program are given trips to the Eli Lilly Plant at Indianapolis, Indiana by the Eli Lilly Company, donor of the health awards.

Report to the President

The National Service Committee coordinates the efforts of the National 4-H Foundation and the Federal Extension Service in planning each year the "Report to the President" of the United States in April, following the Club Congress in the fall.

---

[36]See Appendix for national award sponsors at the 4-H Club Congress since the start of the program.

Careful selection of six Congress delegates is made. The Conrad Hilton Hotel sponsors the trip to Washington, D. C. and New York City. The first Missouri selection for this honor was Frances E. McQueen of Holt County in 1960. In 1964 two members were chosen to make the report in 1965: Melody Richardson of Carroll County, and Charles Humphreys of Saline County.

Chapter VIII

MISSOURI'S CONTRIBUTION

The Major Contribution That This State
Has Made to the National Program

The 4-H program at the state or national level is very flexible. At the national level the age limits are the only standardized features. The 4-H pledge, with slight changes, is used nation-wide.

The objectives of 4-H are universal. But not all state club organizations take the same road to reach these objectives. Every state has made some contribution to the general 4-H club program.

Missouri makes no claims to any "firsts" in the overall 4-H club program. But Missouri has pioneered in 4-H club work. It is listed among the innovators. Robert S. Clough, who started in Extension work in 1917 and became Emeritus Extension Professor in 1958, has observed 4-H club progress almost from the beginning.[37] He is in an enviable position to evaluate Missouri's contributions to the 4-H program.

The structure of the community club is a distinctive Missouri feature. The club is composed of members, a community leader, perhaps an assistant community leader, and as many project leaders as there are project groups within the club. All leaders are adults. Each project group and its project leader meets independent of the club for instruction and training.

The club elects the usual officers: President, vice-president, secretary, treasurer, song and game leader, and one or more to the county 4-H council. The president appoints five standing committees: program committee, membership committee, and three activity committees. Each project group elects a chairman.

It logically follows that meetings conform to the structure. Meetings of the entire club are held once a month all year. The October meeting is usually the annual meeting when officers are elected and committees are appointed. The yearbook is made for the calendar year. Building of the yearbook follows a definite

---

[37]Personal interview by the author with Robert S. Clough, former Missouri State 4-H Club Leader, now retired, University of Missouri Extension Service, Columbia.

procedure and is completed before the first of the new year and made available for the January meeting.

The program committee and the community and assistant leaders plan the program. The standing committees select goals and make suggestions as to what should go into meeting programs in accordance with goals suggested. Mr. Clough says that the November meeting is reserved for meeting of the several committees. Then the club's entire membership selects goals and accepts, or rejects, the committee's recommendations. The program committee plans the program, and assembles and distributes the yearbooks to members.

Project meetings are usually held in homes or on the property of members. Meetings are teaching or practice sessions under the direction of project leaders. Approved practices, judging, demonstrating, and preparation for exhibit take most of the time of these sessions.

The project chairman presides at business sessions. He reports to the club regarding progress, plans, and accomplishments of the project groups. The program committee usually leaves space in the yearbook for contributions by project groups.

It is assumed that all members are interested in health, in fulfillment of their pledge, and that all are also interested in recreation. It is also felt that the additional activity, such as wildlife conservation, safety, or grooming has been selected as an activity of interest to all members. A high percentage of club meeting programs are built around *activities.*

The action and interaction of standing committees often seem to the casual reader to be a sort of regimentation, or seem to be at least too involved for voluntary leaders and committee members to follow. This plan is hardly ever followed exactly. But it is normal procedure in many clubs.

This concept of a community 4-H club would not be acceptable without the support of trained leaders. The very specialized training for community, project, and junior leaders is another unique feature of Missouri's 4-H club program.

The G.M.&O. Railroad sponsored a two-day training conference at Clover Point Camp in the Lake of the Ozarks State Park in the summer of 1949. The conference was especially for the community club leaders of 13 counties served by the railroad. The program for this conference consisted of program planning, developing activities, looking toward group achievement, and meeting the needs of youth.

The Board of Trustees of the newly formed Missouri 4-H Foundation at its first planning meeting in the fall of 1949 decided that this kind of conference should be presented state-wide. Accordingly it proceeded to secure sponsors for five additional meetings in various parts of the state.

Several conferences have been held each year since, and have provided training for 400 to 600 community leaders. Each year more than 1,700 community clubs operate in the state. All community leaders would be reached in the course of three years. It hasn't achieved this fully, but a sizeable majority of club leaders have responded.

County Extension agents embraced the idea of community clubs from the start and followed up with training at the county level. An amazing amount of talent was found among leader groups. Their influence was genuinely felt, county-wide.

Training of project leaders followed a different pattern. Many series of meetings were held with project leaders in all home economics, meat animal, dairy, tractor, electricity, and other projects. In recent years the practice has been to shift to specialists who work with county agents, who in turn, work directly with voluntary leaders.

The Missouri concept of junior leadership has made many contributions to total development of this phase of 4-H club work. Mr. T. T. Martin (Missouri State Leader, 1923-1943, and 4-H club agent, 1943-1954) wrote the first junior leadership publication which was used throughout the United States to develop this phase of the 4-H club program.

Missouri was one of the first states to develop a comprehensive plan for involving junior leaders in leadership positions at both local and county levels. These include active leadership in project work, activities, recreation, and organizational processes.

To support and reinforce the junior leadership movement, a state-wide leadship conference was started in 1954. It was held annually until 1958 at which time it evolved into five annual district leadership conferences. The programs were patterned after the state conference. From 1958 to 1964, 3,685 junior leaders attended the conferences.

A large number of counties have active county junior leader councils that meet regularly. In 1964, 78 counties reported 279 meetings for training junior leaders, attended by 6,062. A summary of opportunities for training junior leaders would include the following:

  5 State week-long junior leader conferences
 38 District 4-day junior leader conferences
  5 State wildlife conservation camps for members of conservation standing committees
  5 Health camps especially for chairmen of health committees
  2 State-wide workshops for health committee chairmen
  6 Years of afternoon programs at State Club Week have been devoted to workshops on 4-H activities. Many State Club Week delegates are junior leaders.
279 County meetings for training in 1964.
 39 Bus loads of delegates to National Citizenship Short Courses.

Missouri should be considered among the originators of various features of the junior leader program, including public speaking, standing committees, activities, and the annual junior leader state-wide coverage in junior leader state and district conferences. The assembling of bus loads of delegates to the National Citizenship Short Courses is part of Missouri's junior leader program.

Missouri was one among several innovators of the National 4-H Citizenship Short Course program at the National 4-H Center in Washington, D. C.

It is a matter of record that J. W. Burch, director of the Extension Service in Missouri, 1935-1959, recommended this project to make better use of the facilities of the National Center. Mr. Burch said then that he regretted that Missouri 4-H visits to the national Capitol and its shrines were limited to the four delegates to the National 4-H Conference.

The distinctive feature of Missouri's contribution is in participation or acceptance of the opportunity to make 4-H pilgrimages to the national Capitol. A bus load composed of 4-H members from counties in southwest Missouri attended in 1960, the first year. A bus load consisted of about 35 club members, an Extension agent, and two or more adult leaders. Most of the members making these trips have been junior leaders. A total of 39 bus loads (1,248 members) made this pilgrimage during the 1960-1964 period, the five years since it started.

Figures for 1962 show the state-wide distribution of delegates:

Area	Number Counties	Members	Local Leaders	Agents	Total
Northwest (one Northeast)	11	67	7	3	77
West Central	6	33	3	1	37
Southwest	10	31	4	1	36
East Central	9	57	8	3	68
Totals	36	188	22	8	218

One year the entire delegation of 27 represented Audrain County. Some of the comments by participants aptly illustrate the reaction of those making the trip:

"Twenty-three junior leaders spoke to over 1,000 people about their trip. They took part in five different radio programs and two television programs."

"Talks were made on communism, freedom, and citizenship. Things were introduced which led us into new fields of thinking and where we found greater understanding of our club, our community and our country."

"I know that everyone is now more aware of our government and our freedoms."

"I believe there is a real problem facing freedom. This short course is a very good way to learn our responsibilities."

All delegates visited national shrines, the White House, and the Capitol. All sat in Congressional hearings and legislative sessions. Most were photographed with Missouri Congressmen and dined with them, and all enjoyed making their home for a week at the National 4-H Center."

County camping in Missouri means camping by members from a single county or a group of adjoining counties. It is as old as 4-H itself. Missouri is fortunate in that the State Park Board has provided facilities for 4-H camping in six state parks. One forestry camp is used, and the camp at Lake Wappapello is strictly a 4-H Camp. There are features of the Missouri camping program worth enumerating.

Few states can match the support given 4-H camping by the Missouri Department of Conservation. Outstanding specialists from the field service, educational, and administrative staffs of the Department have been most helpful with the camping program. These men have remained for the entire camp period. Among these is Charles Schwartz, biologist, whose art work, books, and movies have made him internationally known. Another is the late Rudolph Bennett, first head of the wildlife research unit in the Zoology Department of the University of Missouri, who had much to do with establishing the Conservation Department in 1947. In 1959 the Department made available a staff especially equipped to teach conservation in a five-year series. Themes for the series included:

1959 - Homes for Wildlife
1960 - Getting Acquainted with Wildlife
1961 - Hunter Safety
1962 - Boat Safety
1963 - Water Facts and Fishing Skills
1964 - Back to Hunter Safety

A similar teaching program was started in 1964 by the 4-H Electric Program Committee of the Missouri Electrification Council, making use of electric utilities and REA's. In 1959 this committee installed in the 4-H building at the State Fair in Sedalia an air conditioned electric theater. Since then there has been a daily program during State Fair week which consists of demonstrations by 4-H members.

Chapter IX

UNIVERSITY LEADERSHIP

Deans of the University of Missouri College of Agriculture . . .
The Extension Directors . . .
4-H Club State Leaders 1914-1964

In terms of organizational arrangement, much of the responsibility for 4-H club work rests with the Extension Director of the Land Grant University. Until recent trends toward university-wide Extension divisions, the Director reported 4-H plans and progress to the Dean of the College of Agriculture.

In turn, the Director delegated responsibility for developing plans and conducting programs to a state 4-H club leader. Thus, while not directly involved in day-to-day operation of 4-H, the deans and directors played key roles in the overall program by providing leadership and other resources.

Deans of the University of Missouri College of Agriculture during the past half-century have included:

F. B. Mumford, 1909-1938
M. F. Miller, 1938-1945
E. A. Trowbridge, 1945-1948
J. H. Longwell, 1948-1960
E. R. Kiehl, 1960-

The Extension Directors

The Extension Directors, chief administrative officer of the total 4-H program, quite naturally have been men interested in the youth of the state. Missouri has long been recognized for its outstanding directors who have been at the forefront in promoting 4-H.

A.J. Meyer
(1914-1930)

Arthur John Meyer was the first Director of the University of Missouri Cooperative Extension Service. He began his work as director shortly after the passage of the Smith-Lever Act on May 8, 1914.

A. J. Meyer   *R. R. Thomasson*   *J. W. Burch*   *C. B. Ratchford*

Mr. Meyer first came to Missouri in 1911 to act as assistant to the Dean of the Missouri College of Agriculture and to take charge of the "Short Course." The Cooperative Extension Service was organized in 1914, and on June 8, 1914, Mr. Meyer was appointed head of it.

Previous to this time, Extension work was carried on by the various departments. Mr. Meyer did his undergraduate work at the University of Wisconsin, leaving there in his senior year to begin his work at the University of Missouri.

R. R. Thomasson
(1930-1935)

R. R. Thomasson joined the Extension Service staff August 1, 1919, as county agent of Webster County. Following two years' work as a county agent, Thomasson became assistant county agent leader in 1921, state Extension agent in 1924, and assistant director in 1930.

During the five-year period from 1930 to 1935, he was assistant director in charge of Extension work in Missouri. For health reasons Thomasson relinquished his position as assistant director in charge to J. W. Burch, in 1935.

Thomasson was a native of Fredericktown, Missouri, and received his BS degree in agriculture from the University of Missouri in 1917. The two-year period between his graduation in 1917 and his joining the Extension Service in 1919 was spent in World War I Army service as an officer in the Infantry.

Mr. Thomasson died in early 1967, ending long and meritorious service with the Missouri Extension Service.

James W. Burch
(1935-1959)

James W. Burch served for 36 years in the Missouri Extension Service; two years as a county agent, 11 years as animal husbandry specialist, one year as assistant director, and for 24 years as director.

He was reared on a farm in Linn County, Missouri, graduated from the University of Missouri College of Agriculture in 1916, served as a captain in World War I, and farmed for himself for two years before joining the Extension staff. He received an MS degree in agricultural economics from the University of Missouri in 1931.

As Extension Director, he developed and guided an outstanding program of "Balanced Farming" that received national recognition. This program was put into operation on 30,000 Missouri farms.

He inaugurated a plan for rural leaders to set up a state advisory committee to the Extension Service, and for years this committee has suggested improvements for Extension's contribution to the people of Missouri.

Director Burch emphasized that the Extension Service should reach the maximum number of farm families with an educational program designed to fit their needs.

As chairman of the Extension Organization and Policy Committee of the Land Grant College Association in 1943, Mr. Burch played a leading part in obtaining passage of the Bankhead-Flannagan Act, which increased funds for the Extension Service by $12,500,000. He served as Chairman of the Extension Section of the Land Grant College Association in 1951. Mr. Burch died in 1962.

C. B. Ratchford
(1959 to date)
Vice-President of the University of Missouri
for Extension

Dr. C. B. Ratchford was born in Gaston County, North Carolina, in 1920. He holds BS and MS degrees in agricultural economics from North Carolina State College. He received his doctorate in economics from Duke University in 1951.

He served as a captain in the Army during World War II. Two of his four years of service were overseas with the Office of Strategic Services. At present he is a lt. colonel in the Army Reserve.

Before coming to Missouri he was project leader of the North Carolina Cooperative Extension Service's farm management and marketing project, and from 1954 to 1959 was assistant director of the North Carolina Extension Service.

Dr. Ratchford was appointed Director of the Missouri Cooperative Extension Service on July 1, 1959. He was appointed Dean of the University of Missouri's Extension Division when it was formed July 1, 1960.

He was appointed Vice-President of the University of Missouri for Extension in July, 1965. In this position he is responsible for all Extension activities of the entire University of Missouri on four campuses.

His title is: Vice-President of the University of Missouri for Extension; Director, Cooperative Extension Service; and Professor of Agricultural Economics.

State 4-H Club Leaders

Missouri's state 4-H leaders all have been men with an inherent love for young men and women. All have been warm and friendly, endearing them to the state's people. Through their efforts, they have added greatly to the development of the state's most important resource, its young men and women.

R. H. Emberson
(1914-1923)

Richard Huff Emberson was born in Johnson County, Missouri, February 23, 1862, and died in Columbia, Missouri, December 30, 1942. He was a member of the University of Missouri faculty for 33 years.

R. H. Emberson   *T. T. Martin*   *R. S. Clough*   *Frank Graham*

He received his education in the Universities of Missouri, Wisconsin, and Chicago. He was a member of the faculties of various Missouri high schools and the Northeast and Northwest Missouri State Colleges.

After serving as assistant state supervisor of schools from 1904 to 1905, he became assistant professor of rural education at the University of Missouri in 1909 and was appointed to the Extension Service staff in 1914 to organize University 4-H club work on a state-wide basis.

T. T. Martin
(1923-1943)

T. T. Martin was state 4-H leader for the Missouri Cooperative Extension Service for 20 years. He came to the University of Missouri from Springfield, Mass., in 1923.

Reared on an Indiana farm, Mr. Martin attended Indiana State Teachers College at Terre Haute. He taught in rural district and consolidated schools for six years and was county superintendent of schools in Hendricks County, Indiana, for seven years, to 1918. Meanwhile working on his own education, he received a BS Degree from State Teachers College in 1911 and an AB from Central Normal College in 1918.

In the fall of 1918, Mr. Martin began his 4-H club leadership, becoming the first leader of that project for the State of Delaware, where he continued for three and a half years. After two and a half years in regional junior achievement work with urban youth in the New England States, at Springfield, Mass., he came to the University of Missouri in 1923, as 4-H leader of the Extension Service.

For several years Martin has concentrated on research, writing, and teaching in the fields of 4-H leadership, youth motivation, and leader training. He is the author of a series of Extension Studies published by the University of Missouri College of Agriculture. He also wrote an outstanding book, the first in its field, published in 1955, by Harper & Brothers, now Harper & Row, New York, N.Y., entitled, *The 4-H Club Leader's Handbook.*

Robert S. Clough
(1943-1958)

Robert S. Clough was leader of the Missouri Cooperative Extension Service's 4-H club program for 15 years and an Extension worker for 39 years.

Clough began his work as an Extension worker in Kentucky, where he worked as a county agent from 1917 to 1919. Early in 1920 he came to Missouri as county agent in Johnson County. In 1923 he was named county agent in Pettis County, and in 1928 he became county agent of Jackson County.

Clough was agent in Jackson County from 1928 until he resigned in 1937 to become general manager of the Midwest Wool Marketing Association in Kansas City. He also worked as a radio farm commentator and did a series of radio transcriptions that had nation-wide coverage before returning to the Extension Service as state 4-H agent in December, 1939.

He assumed leadership of the Missouri Extension 4-H project in 1943, and served until his retirement in 1958.

Clough served as a member of the National Association of Land Grant Colleges and Universities Sub-Committee on 4-H Club Work during 1956 and 1957. He was chairman of the group the final year.

In 1956 he was presented the United States Department of Agriculture's Superior Service Award.

Frank Graham
(1958-to Date)

Frank Graham was reared on a farm near Fair Grove in Greene County, Missouri. He graduated from the Fair Grove High School in 1938. As a youth he had one year of 4-H club experience and three years of vocational agriculture.

Graham graduated from the University of Missouri College of Agriculture with a BS degree in agriculture in 1942. He became an assistant county agent of Lawrence County on September 15, 1942, and county agent of Wright County, December 9, 1942. He resigned as county agent of Wright County to enlist for service in World War II in May, 1944.

He took basic training in Field Artillery at Fort Sill, Oklahoma, and completed Officer's Candidate School at Fort Benning, Georgia. He was assigned to the 4th Infantry Training Regiment, Parachute School at Fort Benning until discharged in November, 1945.

Graham served as county agent of Johnson County from January 1, 1946, to January 1, 1949, and as state agent and administrative assistant to the Director of Extension from January to July, 1957.

He became a member of the state 4-H club staff where he served as state club agent in the South Central District and as assistant project leader until July 31, 1958. He was appointed state 4-H club leader August 1, 1958. He received an MS degree in Extension Education from the University of Missouri in 1954.

With the exception of one year, he has served as secretary of the Missouri 4-H Foundation from the date of its organization October 10, 1949. The state 4-H club leader also serves as a member of the Foundation's Board of Trustees.

He is a member of Epsilon Sigma Phi, national honorary society for Extension personnel; and Gamma Sigma Delta, national honor society of agriculture.

He was appointed a member of the National 4-H Foundation's Board of Trustees in 1962.

Chapter X

THE LOOK AHEAD

"Today (1969) there are more than one million youths in Missouri between the ages of six and 21. This number is expected to decrease somewhat in the next 10 years. Never before has our state and nation been confronted with such vast human potential in its youth and at the same time possessed the 'know-how' and resources to arrange situations conducive to the development of that potential.[38]

"Based on key national trends, the needs and problems of youth in a modern society fall into the following areas. Youth need to:

1. *Understand, at least partially, the nature of expanding technology.*
2. *Understand the basic principles of decision making.*
3. *Devise a simple scorecard for evaluating personal values.*
4. *Learn how to use the God-given ingredient – TIME.*
5. *Strengthen family life.*
6. *Understand the value of being a part of a group—working and playing together as a group—the values of team work.*
7. *Develop good citizenship traits.*
8. *Develop leadership qualities.*
9. *Have guidelines for professional or career guidance.*
10. *Have a life-long desire for wisdom, beginning with step one—a desire for knowledge."*

*   *   *

In the light of such outstanding achievements in America in the field of 4-H club work during the past half century, foolish indeed would be the author who would attempt to predict what the next half century has in store for this great youth movement. At best it would only be a guess, because the world and all that is in it move too fast for the soothsayer.

---

[38]"Extension Youth Programs" an unpublished guidance paper prepared by the Youth Programs Staff, Extension Division, University of Missouri—1969.

Since club work began in 1914, we have seen corn production per acre increased from a national average of a mere 27 bushels per acre to several times that amount.[39]

In 1914, if a farmer was able to grow 50 bushels of wheat per acre he had achieved a great goal. A bale of cotton per acre was something sought after throughout the South. Today, wheat farmers and the cotton farmers alike consider those yields to be easily attainable, and many times greater yields are reported. Such comparisons can be made in all fields of agriculture.

The great technological and scientific improvements that have come in this century have not passed over the area of food production. In fact, if this country has excelled in anything, it has been in the tremendous production goals achieved in agriculture.

Members of 4-H clubs learn from the very beginning how to produce in project work. Many of the great production goals in various areas of agriculture were achieved first by 4-H club members, using the knowledge provided them by their State Experiment Stations, through their county Extension directors.[40]

The shift in emphasis from "things" to boys and girls is symbolized by two milestones—in 1927 when "4-H" was adopted as the official name of the organization, and in 1938 when the "community type" club became generally acceptable.

The first 50 years of 4-H club work in Missouri have seen it enlarge its scope, moving from the individual project area into the wider field of citizenship development. The individual will not lose his place of importance in the emerging half-century ahead; in fact, the purpose of 4-H is to provide opportunities for the maximum development of the individual, consequently his place in society will be enhanced as a result of the development of his personal competencies.

In the future the picture will likely be changed a bit. Whereas in the last half-century 4-H club girls, who found their project work stressing production of food and clothing for the family, will find in the next half-century more stress being laid on consumer education, family relations, leadership, and citizenship development.

Club boys, who in the past half-century exerted great competitive enterprise in producing 100 bushels of corn on an acre of ground, will in the years ahead place more emphasis on scientific exploration, human relations, and leadership and citizenship development.

Production will not be totally forgotten, however, because food is of the greatest concern to the world today. But more emphasis will be placed upon the development of competent and civic minded boys and girls.

As one Missouri county extension director said recently: "Projects and principles have always been the basis of club work, and in the future principles will probably be emphasized more than projects." Club members will be exposed to many decision making opportunities to test these principles.

---

[39] Article from "Corn", (Corn Industries Research Foundation, Washington, D.C., Vol. XVI, No. 1, "4-H For Good Farming and The Good Life"), 1960.

It is thought that Missouri's youth program workers—at all levels—can best help the young people of this state achieve such goals, as those already indicated, by doing the following:

1. *Enhance the quality of individual decisions and provide the skills needed to carry over the decisions.*

2. *Increase the ability of individuals to interact effectively with others.*

3. *Assist the individual to acquire the ability to utilize community services and to participate in the development of community services.*

4. *Enhance the social, physical, and economic mobility of the individual.*

The University of Missouri Extension Division will continue a comprehensive program flexible in outreach to include all boys and girls regardless of race, creed, geographic location, or economic status.

ACKNOWLEDGMENT

One does not simply write a book. It is not that easy. One sits down, and slowly the book seems to come to life.

But even before that much must have taken place. Facts must be assembled. Facts must be verified. Like the production of a perfect ear of corn, many things happened before the ear of corn appeared upon the stalk, and finally was harvested in the autumn-time.

So a book grows, with many hands making it possible. The author fully realizes this, and gives credit to the following for helping make this story of the first 50 years of Missouri 4-H club work a reality:

Robert S. Clough, former State 4-H Leader, whose outstanding research in bringing together all major facts regarding the history of club work in Missouri, made easy the writing of this book, and to the following for noteworthy assistance:

Paul H. Gwin, associate agriculture editor, who provided the editorial assistance and initiative needed to get this book into print.

T. T. Martin, former State 4-H Leader;

Frank Graham, present State 4-H Leader;

Jane Hinote, former member of the state 4-H staff, and now retired;

Dr. Elmer Ellis, President Emeritus, UMC;

Dr. Richard Brownlee, Director, State Historical Society;

Ralph Angel, Director and Agricultural Agent of Iron County;

Edwin B. Burnham, father of Bonaparte P. Burnham, who organized the first Corn Clubs in Iron County;

Frieda B. Barber, Ironton, Missouri, who assisted in developing the history of the first Corn Clubs in Iron County;

Paul Bernard, Agricultural Director, KMOX-TV, St. Louis;

Theodore Hutchcroft, Information Director, National 4-H Club Foundation, Washington, D. C.;

Vivian Wiser, Historian, Agricultural History Branch, U. S. Department of Agriculture, Washington, D. C.;

Betty Rottman, Columbia, Newswriter, Office of Public Information, UMC;

R. R. Thomasson, deceased, formerly of Columbia;

Ty Thompson, National 4-H Service Committee, Chicago;

Charline Lindsay, Extension Youth Specialist.

Dr. C. B. Ratchford, Dr. John Longwell, Dr. Elmer Kiehl, Dr. Richard Lee, and *Dr. Delmar Hatesohl,* all members of the University of Missouri faculty at Columbia;

Dr. John F. McGowan, Dean of Extension Division, UMC;

Mrs. Oliver Howard, and *Mrs. J. E. Comfort,* Reference Librarians, State Historical

Society of Missouri, Columbia; and present and past members of the Cooperative Extension Staffs, including:

Flora Lee Carl, T. A. Ewing, A. F. Stephens, J. U. Morris, F. E. Rodgers, A. C. Ausherman, John Burkeholder, Nelson Trickey, George P. Rowe, J. Ross Fleetwood and *Hugh L. Nutt.*

The author wishes to thank the many newspapers, radio and TV stations, and magazines in Missouri, and nearby states, who gave publicity to this project and made possible the unearthing of valuable material regarding the early history of 4-H club work in Missouri.

The author especially wishes to thank every member of the Missouri 4-H Foundation, its Board of Trustees, and Advisory Committee, for inspiration and endorsement of this work.

There are individuals who as the writing progressed, "went the extra mile" in assisting with this project, and to them the author owes especially a word of thanks, and acknowledgement. They are:

H. T. Harlin, Gainesville; J. Rogers Cochran, Columbia; Don K. Spalding, St. Joseph; Mrs. E. Y. Crouch, Liberty; Ray Miller, Osage Beach; Amy Kelly, Columbia; Cordell Tindall, Fayette; James W. Stephens, Kansas City; Virgil Burk, Columbia; E. G. Cherbonnier, St. Louis; J. C. Welman, Kennett; Jack Wright, Columbia; E. C. Adams, Blue Springs; Mrs. J. W. Burch, Columbia; D. Howard Doane, Point Lookout; James Kirkpatrick, Windsor; John Sam Williamson, Columbia; Oliver Ferguson, Fredericktown; W. W. Alexander, Trenton; Gordon Gillispie, St. Louis; Scott Meyer, Hannibal; J. Ed Rutter, Newark, N. J.; Karl M. Wickstrom, Marshfield; Clyde Brown, Laddonia; Professor Val Thiessen of the University of Oklahoma City, and to all the others who by letter or word of encouragement made contributions to this effort.

Board of Trustees, The Missouri 4-H Foundation: James C. Kirkpatrick, Chm., Jefferson City; J. C. Welman, Vice-Chm., Kennett; J. Rogers Cochran, Treas., Columbia; Ray W. Call, Cape Girardeau; E. G. Cherbonnier, St. Louis; Mrs. E. Y. Crouch, Kansas City; D. Howard Doane, Point Lookout; H. T. Harlin, Gainesville; Don K. Spalding, St. Joseph; James W. Stephens, Kansas City; John Sam Williamson, Columbia; Jackson A. Wright, Columbia.

Advisory Committee, The Missouri 4-H Foundation: E. C. Adams, Blue Springs; Willis Alexander, Wash., D.C.; George Avant, Springfield; Clyde Brown, Laddonia; Mrs. J. W. Burch, Columbia; Gordon Gillespie, East St. Louis; Miss Amy Kelly, Columbia; Mrs. C. C. McGennis, Rich Hill; Ray E. Miller, Osage Beach; R. D. Pennewell, Palmyra; J. C. Penney, New York; H. Lang Rogers, Joplin; J. E. Rutter, Newark, N. J.; G. B. Thorne, Linneus; Cordell Tindall, Fayette; Billy Joe West, Kansas City; Homer A. Young, Kansas City.

To each the author acknowledges their contributions and realizes that without the efforts of all these, and others lost in memory, this work would not have been possible.

BY ROBERT S. CLOUGH
4-H CLUB LEADER EMERITUS

EPILOGUE

We live in deeds not years;
in thoughts, not breaths.

– Phillip J. Bailey

An epilogue is a poem or speech at the conclusion of a play. This book is the record of a great play, one that has had all of the highlights of a Shaksperean drama in the 50 years it has been "on stage" not only in Missouri, but throughout America. Missouri's 4-H story is one small piece of the rich tapestry, constituting this great youth program throughout our land.

The following pages were selected especially to be inlcuded in this part of the book—The Epilogue—from the many records of Missouri 4-H members, covering 50 years from 1914 to 1964. These pages may contain anecdotes and records of projects that may make you smile, others that may sadden you a bit, but regardless of how they affect you as you read them, they are the little nuggets that one person selected for inclusion here.

You as the reader may know of other 4-H club records and incidents, and wonder why they are not included, but every "high" and every "low" of Missouri's 4-H record, of course, could not be included in one small volume. If the very one that you recall is not included, just know that for some reason it did not come to the attention of the one who selected the following at random, and after much reading, from club records in Columbia.

The person who did all of the combing of the records to secure the incidents, anecdotes, facts, and fun gathered in these next pages, was for many years connected with Missouri 4-H club work as its state leader, and has been more closely identified with the program than any other living man or woman.

Sandra Goes to Camp

Sandra was 11 years old, and had just become a member of a 4-H club. She was enrolled in the ABC's of clothing and was very enthusiastic about all of her club work.

There was to be a 4-H camp in July and Sandra wanted very much to go. There wasn't much ready cash from her family's little Ozark farm. The pick-up truck had been sold to pay the last of the indebtedness. The team and wagon was now their method of transportation.

Mr. and Mrs. McGarrity thought Sandra should go to 4-H camp if she really wanted to go. They talked it over and agreed that if their daughter helped her father in the field to get the cane clean, had her project work done, and could pick and sell enough blackberries to pay the expense of the camp and the bus fare to and from Cabool and Houston, she could go to camp.

Blackberries were plentiful, the price good, and the mail carrier took the berries at 40 cents a gallon and sold them in Cabool. So, the money was soon earned.

July 17 was the eventful day. Sandra was up early to catch her ride with the milk truck to Cabool. Then she went to the bus station to take her first bus ride. The bus was late—one hour late. The letter said the cars would leave Houston at 1 p.m. Would they wait for her bus, or was she going to miss the trip she had worked so hard to earn?

As the bus pulled into the station, a little girl, carrying a suitcase and a roll of bedding, looked anxiously about as she stepped from the bus. Her face soon broke into a smile when she saw her home demonstration agent waiting for her. Sandra had a wonderful experience and often recalled years later her thrills that summer of 1945 when she attended her first 4-H club camp.

Evelyn's Darning Story

A clothing club was organized in the Coldwater Community during the depression years of "the thirties."

The 11 clothing club girls came from small farms where the incomes were small and there was very little money for new clothing. So it was necessary that they learn to repair and remake old clothing.

Evelyn Ward was 11 years old when she joined the club. She was very interested in the project and tried very hard to perfect her work.

One of the requirements in the second year was to be able to apply a patch and to know how to darn. She soon learned to do almost perfect darning.

After she graduated from high school, she went to St. Louis and got a job in a large cleaning establishment. One day the floor manager came through asking for someone to do darning. It seems none of the women knew how to darn. Evelyn spoke up and said that she could darn and the lady laughed and didn't believe her. But when Evelyn assured the manager that she knew how, she was given something to darn. When the manager saw the work, she said "Where did you learn to darn like that?"

Evelyn said she learned it in a 4-H club. The floor manager had never heard of a 4-H club and wanted to know what it was. Evelyn explained. The lady called the other floor managers to see the darning.

Soon Evelyn was given a job as floor manager and she worked there for several years until after her marriage.

Wenda "Moves" Her Garden

The most unusual thing that happened in club work in Holt County in 1936 was the "moving" done in June by Wenda Alton of the Fortesque Club. Wenda was only 11 years old and a very little girl, but a most industrious one.

When it was necessary for her family to move after her 4-H garden was planted and growing well, she was almost heartbroken. However, she wasn't to be daunted by a little thing like that. With the help of a big brother, a spade and plenty of boxes, the garden was moved to the new home. The plants moved included 15 of kale, 30 kohlrabies, a long row of salsify, a number of broccoli, parsley, cabbage, okra, peppers, tomatoes, cucumbers, garlic, and 500 Bermuda onions.

When her home demonstration agent said, "Why Wenda, how did you do it?", she calmly answered, "We just dug up plenty of dirt with the plants and then watered them until it rained."

Gardening

In Randolph County in 1943, Lloyd and Everett Koestler produced 18,536 plants of approved varieties from their farms' large hotbeds and sold the plants to neighbors. In war time, that was a distinct service.

In Jasper County in 1946, Leroy Block, 9 years old, did the work in the family garden which produced all the fresh vegetables for a family of 11, plus 400 quarts for winter use. He had 12 different kinds of vegetables in his 4-H garden project.

Four hundred and fifty Negro 4-H members in southeast Missouri were enrolled in 4-H vegetable projects in 1957. Many produced tomatoes for market. Most of them followed the pattern of soil testing, fertilizing, pruning, spraying, staking, and wrapping for market.

In Ray County, in 1957, Larry Hicks of the Henrietta Club, chose watermelons for his vegetable project. Larry produced a total of 20 tons of melons and reported a labor income of $175.

In Cape Girardeau County in 1952, eight 4-H clubs planted 8,000 trees along roadsides and around ponds.

Larry Garrison, Jasper County, sold the top crate of 4-H strawberries in 1957 for $42. Twenty members grew 1,000 plants each.

*   *   *

Articles exhibited at the State Fair in 1957 included air compressors made from old refrigerator motors and parts. The compressors are used on the farm to inflate tires, do spraying, and other work. Other items exhibited included portable yard lamps, portable motors, and brooders.

*   *   *

In his electricity project in 1948, Jimmy Sutherland, 16, 4-H club boy of Johnson County, showed unusual initiative in developing a miniature, properly lighted farmstead. The farmstead was built to scale. It was uniquely designed for display. It attracted much attention at the Missouri State Fair, and it was taken to the 4-H Club Congress for exhibit. Jimmy received a great amount of national, state, and local publicity.

*   *   *

The Salem Club in Greene County held its annual ride in 1960 with 185 horses and wagons.

In 1963, district 4-H horseshows were held for the first time in connection with the Ozark Empire Fair at Springfield and the Mercer District Fair.

*   *   *

Buddy Crews, a 4-H member in Howard County said in 1961, "Since I took this automotive care project, it has been my job to wash, wax, and keep our car clean. I have made a study of road hazards in our community. I have studied state laws. I have studied the engine to understand how it runs. I have figured the cost of a car for a year, or a period of years."

*   *   *

Joe Scott Daniels, in Shelby County in 1948, made a profit of $75 on his 10 colonies of bees in his 4-H bee project. He harvested 400 pounds of honey.

*   *   *

In 1931 in Howard County, C. L. Buoy, Jr., said: "I organized a farm management club among the boys in my community. We were to keep records on our fathers' farms for the following year." (Note: C. L. lost his life in military service in World War II).

*   *   *

Mary Cook, Newton County, in 1938 had completed six years of 4-H clothing work. She reported: "This year I made my mother a coat and four dresses, two of which were wool and the other two were silk."

The next year, in 1939, Donalee Wheale of St. Louis County said, "Last winter I made 20 pleated skirts and five dresses for girlfriends. I make practically all my clothes."

*   *   *

Catherine O'Banion, Nodaway County, reported in 1943: "When I was in the dress revue, I was thoroughly inspected, not only my dress, but also my coiffure, my posture, my shoes, and my carriage. I realized that the dress must not only be of good quality but the person must add to the attractiveness of the costume."

*   *   *

In 1943 in Shelby County, one finds the following in the record: "A pair of uncle's white linen knickers, an attractive blue and white print mash sack with a linen-like texture plus a quarter's worth of findings and a good deal of ingenuity gave Dorothy Sue Hall a blue ribbon in the remodeled section of the dress revue at County Round-Up. The only findings Dorothy bought were a spool of white thread and a card of snaps. She ripped hooks and eyes for the skirt and white pearl buttons for the blouse off an old dress."

And this from the 1945 records of Ste. Genevieve County: "Starting with an old outmoded three-quarter length fishtail jacket and a straight skirt with split pleats at the side, Mary Linden made herself a dressmaker suit and saved $15 or more. This member spent four hours cutting the garment. She had to piece the underneath part of the sleeve five times but by careful pressing each time a piece was added that was not noticeable. There was not a scrap left larger than three by six inches but the finished product is certainly worthy of Mary's work. She won a red ribbon on this remade suit at the County Fair."

*   *   *

Betty Hofferman of Pettis County in 1936 said: "Up until the time I joined a canning club, my family had not canned an adequate supply of meats and vegetables for an adequate diet. While demonstrating, judging, and exhibiting are important, I consider the planning, canning, and storage of foods to fill the required health budget the most important. Now I plan our family budget and help plan and plant the garden to meet this budget. In spite of two dry years, I have canned 417 quarts of fruits and vegetables and stored 16 bushels of vegetables with an estimated value of $80."

*   *   *

Cleta Brundage in Caldwell County said in 1938: "What I consider my greatest achievement is making bread. Few people can make good bread."

*   *   *

In 1947, Juanita Davison of Dallas County said this: "I like to prepare a dinner from my canned foods. It seems so much better to go to the cellar and get your own canned foods instead of going to town to buy it."

*   *   *

The State Canning Champion in 1951 was Carolyn Risser of Nodaway County, who canned 360 quarts of food for her family.

That same year Shirley Bechter of Andrew County not only did most of the family canning but also helped her grandmother and neighbors. She canned food for the family minister who was a bachelor.

*   *   *

Marilyn Marsh, Macon County, in 1952 won national honors with her demonstration, "Milk Throughout The Day."

*   *   *

Rosemary Myer, Nodaway County, reported in 1947 that she had taken food preparation projects for seven of her nine years of 4-H work. In that time she had prepared 3,386 dishes, 277 meals, and 475 breakfasts.

*   *   *

In 1955 Rosemary Hulshof, New Madrid County, in her food preservation project canned 4,365 quarts; froze 480 fryers and 1,865 pounds of beef, fish, and pork; and stored 430 bushels for her nine-member family. Rosemary has twelve brothers and sisters.

*   *   *

Clyda Conrad, Buchanan County said in her report in 1939: "This completes my fourth year of home grounds work. My entire family and myself have benefited from this work. After all the members of the family became interested we worked together toward a common goal—making an outdoor living room. It is almost unbelievable now, as we enjoy picnics and entertain friends in this room, to think that four years ago it was a pen for baby chicks."

*   *   *

In Clay County in 1955, Flora Duncan made a bedroom for her brother out of a storeroom. It took detailed planning to get the desired results in a room with dormer window and slanted ceiling.

*   *   *

Betty Back of Saline County, in 1957, at the age of 14, purchased a maple chair for 50 cents, refinished it, and reseated it, using sea grass.

*   *   *

In 1962 Barbara Bird, Dade County, said: "I am proud to have a room of my own which I redecorated. I have learned many things about decorating—how to give the appearance of a large room by the use of paint, how to choose accessories that complement my room, and how to use old furniture to redecorate with, which saves me money but still looks sharp. I have a room that expresses my personality."

*   *   *

During the Leonard Club Achievement Program in August of 1945, which honored 19 former 4-H members from the Leonard Club, a gold star was placed on the flag in honor of Lt. Willis Griffith killed in action in World War II.

Lt. Griffith and five other former members of the Armed Forces were charter members of the first 4-H club in Shelby County, organized in 1935.

*   *   *

In 1955, Ralls County 4-H members took over the operations of the county courthouse for a day.

*   *   *

Melvin Wahl, Warren County, in 1940, reported: "In the winter of 1939-1940 I fed 40 quail at two stations. One of the stations was a low bushy cedar tree and the other was a hog house under a bushy oak tree. I had trouble with the foxes catching the quail when they were in their shelters. I kept traps for the foxes but did not succeed in catching one. Later I demonstrated a system that would provide ample food, cover, and water for two club groups and two farm groups in the community. There are now twice as many quail on the farm as when I first tried to shelter and feed them."

*   *   *

David P. Young, Howard County, tells how drouth nearly defeated his wildlife conservation efforts: "In the summer of 1934, the springs, ponds, creeks, and wells were going dry. We had a large pond that was well stocked with fish but that year it went dry, killing hundreds of fish. We had another severe drouth in 1936."

The government built a large pond 2½ miles from the home. This sparked new enthusiasm in wildlife activities. By 1940, club members interested in wildlife had developed three wildlife areas, planted a windbreak, planted foodbearing shrubs, and helped restore wildlife of the community. "We," says David, "found that when food, cover, and water were provided, wildlife came."

*   *   *

Perry County 4-H Clubs in 1943 were the first to cooperate with the Audobon Society and the Garden Club in establishing five bluebird trails.

*   *   *

On a Sunday afternoon, October 22, 1950, nine members and five leaders of the Beaver 4-H Club, in Ray County, put up 22 bluebird houses between Richmond and Orrick. The houses were made by 17 members enrolled in the woodwork project.

*   *   *

George Barnitz of Dent County, said at the close of the State 4-H Conservation Camp in 1951: "I learned all about farm pond planting. I also learned to square dance which I think is quite an accomplishment."

*   *   *

In 1957, in Cass County, 600 quail chicks were distributed to 42 club members who cared for the chicks until they were four weeks old. At that time they were released on 4-H member farms where they had sufficient feed and water to survive.

*   *   *

In 1938, A. H. Orr, Saline County, started a program designed to stimulate 4-H courtesy. A secret committee of five worked all year to determine the most courteous boy and girl, using a score card for evaluation. The score card included introductions, spirit of friendliness, table manners, health, and a quotation: "Remember that a human being cannot be perfect but should be worthy of respect, admiration, and affection."

*   *   *

The Hagers Greene 4-H Club of Shelby County renovated the Copenhaven School into a Community Center in 1942.

*   *   *

The Jones Creek 4-H Club, Newton County, helped collect 10 tons of scrap metal and one ton of scrap rubber in 1942.

*   *   *

In 1943, 4-H club members in Randolph County helped relieve some of the labor shortage by shearing 11,000 sheep.

A total of 209 pounds of silk and nylon hosiery was collected by seven 4-H community clubs in Scotland County during the war year of 1943.

*   *   *

In the heat of war in 1944, 4-H members in Scotland County took their responsibilities seriously. In addition to saving food and fiber, members bought $211,191 worth of war bonds and stamps, sold $108,321 worth of bonds to others, and collected 170 tons of scrap metal.

*   *   *

Four-H members collected 97,285 pounds of waste fat and collected 18,861 bags of milkweed pods in Bates County.

*   *   *

In 1950, the Mill Creek Club, Phelps County, wired the church, cleared the ground in the church yard, and planted shrubs.

*   *   *

Lakenan Woodworking boys, in Shelby County, made and painted 300 wooden blocks in 1951. These were distributed to an orphanage and to other underprivileged children.

*   *   *

The Rise Oak Club of Wright County, in 1955, bought the old Post Oak School building and developed it into a club house.

The Glensted 4-H Club of Morgan County, in 1955, converted an eyesore next to the Glenstead Church, into an attractive picnic area with flower beds, picnic tables, and outdoor area to play.

The Half-way Club of Bates County, in 1956, remodeled an old store building and made a 4-H club house out of it.

*   *   *

The Bunceton 4-H Club of Cooper County tested and treated all the wells in the community in 1948. Five members made the test and treated the wells with chemicals provided by the Boonville Water Department. They then retested to make certain the water was safe.

*   *   *

In 1951, the Matthews 4-H Club in New Madrid County held a dog vaccination clinic. Fifty dogs were given anti-rabies shots.

*   *   *

Bob and Leon Todd, Shelby County, in 1945 made practical use of their woodwork project. Bob built a hayrack, a salt box, several gates, and feed troughs. Both boys built the bed for a rubber tired trailer.

The Shawan Club of Stoddard County in 1955, had four families of woodchucks nesting in their woodchuck houses erected as a part of their conservation activity.

*   *   *

The Guthrie Club of Callaway County, 1953, set a health goal of 100 percent of 4-H families using only milk that had been pasteurized and from cows tested for Bangs disease. At the beginning of the year only one family used pasteurized milk; however, at the end of the year, 36 percent of the club families were pasteurizing their milk and 90 percent had their cows tested for Bangs disease.

*   *   *

Dick DeShon, chairman of the 4-H Health Committee of Buchanan County in 1953, headed the blood donor drive in February. Ten clubs participated and 451 persons gave blood.

*   *   *

The Pleasant Day 4-H Club of Marion County reported in 1953 that 30 adults and older members completed a first aid course.

*   *   *

Karen Kay Price, Benton County, in 1956, inspired by state health camp which she attended, led her community club in an intensive health program. Her club sponsored a rabies clinic for three years.

Twenty-four members have had eye tests, conducted a cancer education program, and demonstrated pasteurization of milk.

*   *   *

The Health work in the Pleasant Day Community in Marion County, in 1959, was directed by Betty Sparks, junior leader. Betty made a health survey and found that only two of the nine families had adequate first-aid supplies. So Betty and her health committee set a goal and made plans to see that each family got a first aid kit. The committee created awareness of the need for first-aid supplies with a skit, supplied cigar boxes for the kits, and demonstrated preparation of different items. The program was climaxed with an exhibit night when skits were judged. Each family exhibited a well-supplied, conveniently arranged first-aid kit.

*   *   *

In Cass County in 1954, 4-H square dances were held the first and third Saturday nights of each month, October to May. Different clubs made the arrangements each time. Average dance attendance was 115 for the year.

*   *   *

In 1946, Cape Girardeau County 4-H Clubs organized a county-wide chorus for 4-H boys and girls. Bi-monthly rehearsals were held with a paid director.

Eugene Coffman, Ste. Genevieve County, in 1944, was awarded a county honor medal for his activities in 4-H safety work. These are the things he did: rebuilt old porch steps, cleaned up loose boards with nails in them, bought a fire extinguisher, grounded a broken lightning rod, made a hook so that a lantern light could be hung in the barn, marked fuel barrels, burned rubbish, and scattered damp hay to prevent excessive heating.

*   *   *

In Gasconade County, in 1960, junior leaders conducted two vehicle safety checks. At check points, 200 vehicles were looked over for faulty parts.

*   *   *

In 1952, Franklin Harris, an 18-year-old boy from Sullivan County had five economy beef steers and a cow herd of four. His meat animal projects during his 4-H experience had a total value of $13,083.

*   *   *

Kendall and Donald Anderson, brothers from Cass County, had Shorthorn champion and reserve champion at the American Royal 4-H Show in 1953. Kendall was awarded a $300 scholarship by Armour and Company for excellence at the National 4-H Livestock Judging Contest held at the International Livestock Exposition in Chicago.

*   *   *

It took Jimmy and Eddie Hammonds of Putnam County exactly one year to finish for market 10 head of beeves in 1955. These calves gained two pounds a day over the entire period and sold for $21.50 a hundredweight. The two tied for honors at the Young Cattlemen's Sale.

*   *   *

Jim Sprake, Buchanan County, showed a net gain of 242 pounds and $72 net profit per steer in his Junior Cattlemen Project in 1956. The goal in this project is to produce choice to good market beef with a minimum of grain feed.

*   *   *

Johnny Saunders, DeKalb County, had a colorful 4-H career. He was a delegate to National 4-H Conference at Washington, D. C., delegate to National 4-H Club Congress, tied for first place in the Western Tractor Operators Contest, and in 1957 made a profit of $111.25 a head on his five steers in the Young Cattleman project.

*   *   *

Roy Pittrich, a 4-H club boy of Cole County, left fatherless at theage of 17, is the manager of his mother's 240-acre farm, and is building on a foundation that his father left. This was reported in 1941.

From modest beginnings in 1938, he developed a registered herd of Aberdeen Angus valued at present (1941) at $1,275. Roy says that it was through 4-H club work that he developed a desire to assume the management and development of his father's Angus herd.

The backing of a good mother, the counsel of an interested grandfather, and close relationship with his county agent, enabled Roy Pittrich to take his place as a leading citizen in his community while yet in his teens.

* * *

In 1940 it was reported that 16 years before, Rollie Thomas had his first contact with the Extension Service when K. G. Harman, Extension specialist from the Missouri College of Agriculture and the Missouri Corn Grower's Association, and the Pettis County Extension Agent were met at the highway by Rollie and his three-year-old-son in a wagon.

The road leading to the house was not passable with an automobile that day. On the way up the hill, Rollie said that one day he wanted to win first place at the International Hay and Grain Show at Chicago, and if he couldn't, perhaps his boy could. The Extension men held straight faces and chuckled inside thinking here was a man who was doing some big talking. However, in 1939, this same boy, as an older 4-H club boy, won first place in the junior section in his division at the International Hay and Grain Show.

* * *

Jerome Johanning, Howard County, had the highest corn yield in that county in 1955 — 134 bushels from his 4-H plot. C. G. Hargin had a yield of 104 bushels to the acre.

* * *

Linda Alkine, Buchanan County, won the Chicken of Tomorrow contest at the State Fair. The average weight of her birds when marketed at eight weeks was 3.6 pounds, with 2.3 pounds of feed necessary to gain one pound. Feed cost was 11 cents per pound.

* * *

There were fourteen ton-litters exhibited by 4-H club members at the St. Joseph Baby Beef and Pig Show in 1938. Doyle Davis, Holt County, merited first recognition based on daily litter gain and type. His ton-litter consisted of 12 crossbred Poland China-Durocs that weighed 3,280 pounds at 201 days.

* * *

John Rush, county agent of Chariton County, said in 1939: "Ralph Austin, Merton Bartelson, Neilson Hart, J. Marvin Garner, and W. D. Price, all of the Mendon Sow and Litter Club of Chariton County, exhibited 20 of their spring pigs which attracted much attention. Of particular interest were the Chester White litters.

"Hart's gilt saved 12 pigs and Garner's gilt saved 10. These excellent type pigs weighing better than 200 pounds at 5½ months indicate conclusively that large litters of pigs farrowed on clean ground and fed properly are the surest means of producing pork economically."

"Please Uncle Charley"

"I couldn't think of going to the Interstate Show. I've accompanied the calves and pigs from Atchison County every year for the past 15 or 20 years. The 4-H'ers don't need me," was the response of Charles Broermann, 4-H leader, at the 1945 Atchison County Livestock Show.

"Please, Uncle Charley" (as all of the 4-H'ers knew him), chorused a number of the members. "We couldn't begin to beat Nodaway and Sullivan Counties in the Carlot Class without your telling us what to do. Please, Uncle Charley."

"If you really think you need me, maybe I can arrange to go," he replied after much urging. "Mother, will you pack a suitcase and send it by one of the parents tomorrow," he said to his wife, Cora. "It's already packed and in the trunk of your car," she replied.

"What do you know—she knew all of the time I couldn't stay away," he said. He went and they won. As long as his health permitted, one man you would always see urging the members on was Charles W. Broermann.

*   *   *

In clothing work I learned to sew and I am now able to do the greater part of the family sewing. Through 4-H I have developed better taste in the selection of my clothing by judging colors and styles best suited to me. A working knowledge of how to prepare and serve a well balanced meal as well as the knowledge of foods needed for a healthy body was learned in foods. All these activities, I believe, have helped in the development of more initiative, tact, and other qualities of leadership.

Anita Zagrodsky, Buchanan County
1930, Delegate to 4-H Conference

*   *   *

I have developed a profitable dairy herd of my own in 4-H dairy project work. I have received awards on exhibits at the Missouri State Fair, the American Royal and the National Dairy Show. I was a member of the State Dairy Judging Team in 1928, and of the State Champion Dairy Demonstration teams that participated at the National Dairy Demonstration Contest at Memphis, Tennessee.

E. C. Adams, Jr., Blue Springs
1932, Delegate to National 4-H
Conference

*   *   *

During my eight years of 4-H experience I have won three championships on exhibits, ten firsts, eight seconds, five thirds, three fourths, and nine other placings. I was alternate on the State Champion Livestock Judging Team in 1930. I was a member of the high ranking demonstration team two years at State 4-H Roundup. I made a net profit of $731 and was awarded $384 in premium money.

Harold Thieman, Lafayette County
1932-Delegate to National 4-H
Conference

As a result of my trips to the American Royal, Conservation Camp, National 4-H Club Congress, and the University of Missouri, I decided to go to college. I entered the University of Missouri College of Agriculture in 1942.

Ralph Wittmeyer, Blue Ridge
1942

* * *

Every bit of the work that I have put into cooking, forestry, entomology, and sewing has been worthwhile. I have advanced my education by it. The nicest part of attending the Round-Up, camps, and Congress has been meeting 4-H members from all over the state and the United States. I think 4-H work is a wonderful investment for the youth of today and tomorrow.

Lavonne Brown
1942, State Dress Revue Girl

* * *

I have greatly enjoyed my work with butterflies. I have 26 specimens which include 13 butterflies and 13 moths. Among the most interesting are the Buckeye and Red Admiral butterflies and the Luna and Hawk moths.

Margaret Malee, Oak Grove

* * *

Probably one of the hardest tasks in life is learning how to win without feeling superior to those who lost and to lose without feeling the judge was unfair. We, as club members, have learned to congratulate the winner instead of complaining if defeated. This attitude is hard at first, but over several years' training, it becomes a part of one's character. In the words of this Club's motto, "learn to win without bragging and to lose without squealing."

Roy Lentz, Independence
1933

* * *

Ronnie Whilfield, Pemiscot County, picked 3,800 pounds of seed cotton per acre from his two-acre patch in 1955. He used land that had been in alfalfa for four years and applied 400 pounds of 12-12-12 fertilizer according to soil tests.

That same year five Gasconade County boys meant business when they produced corn as follows:

George Oelschlaeger on 5 acres, 105 bushels to the acre.
Tom Hoffman on 9 acres, 114 bushels to the acre.
Robert Bohl on 2 acres, 109 bushels to the acre.
Donald Oeschlaeger on 5 acres, 97 bushels to the acre.
Arthur Kopp on 1 2/3 acres, 99 bushels to the acre.

* * *

Leon Rigings, Shelby County, produced 140 bushels to the acre in the 1959 corn yield contest. There were 33 boys entered in this contest.

Wayne Hartman, Nodaway County, more than doubled his yield of corn in 1960 by the use of fertilizer. His fertilized corn yielded 111 bushels to the acre while the unfertilized plot yielded 54 bushels.

Paul Webb of Franklin County in a similar test got 53 bushels to the acre on the untreated plot and 80 bushels on the fertilized acre.

*   *   *

The Whetkins boys of Pemiscot County got their start in college producing cotton, the report of 1960 says. Howard, Tom, Van Lee, Joe Bob, Tommy, and Benny all joined their 4-H Club at the age of 10. "Each year these boys enter the cotton contest and the proceeds from their crop go into a savings account. The boys have produced more than two bales of cotton per acre in the last couple of years," the report reads.

*   *   *

Dent County's successful 4-H Ewe and Lamb Clubs broke down the tradition in that county in 1939 that sheep were ill adapted to Dent County because of dogs.

*   *   *

Clarence Ray of Audrain County started his ewe and lamb project in 1937. At the close of his 1941 club year he had 24 head of sheep and $100 in the bank from lamb sales.

*   *   *

Seven counties in Northeast Missouri cooperated in 1941 in launching a ewe and lamb 4-H program. One thousand seventy-six bred ewes were distributed to 563 boys and girls. The program was expanded to involve half the counties in the state in later years.

*   *   *

Charlene and Caroline Grizer, Holt County, marketed 24 lambs at the St. Joseph 4-H Lamb Marketing Day in 1946. All graded "choice" and averaged 111 pounds. The ewe flock from which these lambs came helped to put these young ladies through the University of Missouri.

*   *   *

Don Rutter, age 15, Shelby County, in 1946, had 20 Shropshire ewes in his sheep project that grossed $534. He raised 29 lambs for a 145 percent lamb crop and clipped nine pounds of wool per head.

*   *   *

Julian Larrick, Shelby County, in 1954 consigned 33 lambs to the St. Louis lamb marketing day. It was the largest consignment at that event that year.

*   *   *

The Drexel Dairy Calf Club (Cass and Bates Counties), distributed 72 dairy calves on the opening day of the event in 1918.

The most outstanding 4-H dairy project member of Pettis County and probably of Missouri is Paul Selken who was a member of an advanced dairy project and leader of a beginners' dairy project. Paul became a dairy club member in 1933, using money earned by trapping rabbits to purchase his first Holstein heifer. He now has a good herd of registered cattle of his own.

* * *

Jefferson County probably represents the most continuous 4-H dairy club development in Missouri. In 1923 the dairy club was organized. As a direct result of this club, a milk truck route was started to St. Louis.

* * *

Danny Shilling, Newton County, in 1953 compared a well-bred registered Jersey cow to a good grade cow. His registered Jersey returned $214 above feed cost, the grade cow $187.

* * *

Bill Rader, county agent of Laclede County in 1960, had this to say about the five delegates to the 4-H Dairy Conference and Tour: "These were about the best six young people I have had the pleasure to know. They are all capable, well mannered, a lot of fun, and able to absorb parts of the program that will always be of value to them."

* * *

The Poultry Club of Montreal (Henry County), in 1918, enrolled 52 members. Every member finished all records and reports, and entered the second year of club work. Four demonstration teams from this club were trained by the local leader.

* * *

Norma Jo Peterman, Saline County, represented Missouri in the National Poultry Production Contest and placed as second alternate in 1948. Norma Joe and her sister Shirley have been in the poultry business for five years and have handled some 7,000 birds in their projects.

* * *

Bert E. Roth, Jr., St. Clair County, handled 120,000 broilers and layers during the five years preceding 1948.

* * *

Juanita Smith, Cooper County, said in 1950 that poultry would have to finance her college career. The egg money from 500 birds in a poultry mamangement project did the trick.

* * *

Eleven Carter County 4-H members raised 800 boilers in homemade brooders and range shelters in 1953. All members made a profit but most money was realized by members who dressed and sold the birds in town.

Deanna Borron, Sullivan County, won the National Federation Youth Achievement scholarship with her turkey project in 1958.

*   *   *

Billy Lee Clemens, Cooper County, produced a pound of gain in his broiler project with 2.1 pounds of feed in 1959.

APPENDIX

4-H STAFF MEMBERS
1914-1964

	From	To
R. H. Emberson	June, 1914	December, 1942
Addie D. Root	April, 1915	July, 1919
George W. Reavis	July, 1918	November, 1919
Frank Wright	November, 1917	February, 1921
Olga Hungate Ronzone	November, 1917	June, 1920
W. L. R. Perry	November, 1918	April, 1920
Grace Dulaney Becker	September, 1920	August, 1922
T. T. Martin	October, 1923	September, 1953
Jane Hinota	June, 1933	August, 1949
Sara Chiles Harned	July, 1925	July, 1932
Margaret C. Huston Tuller	April, 1927	September, 1929
J. Ross Fleetwood	July, 1930	October, 1934
E. T. Itschner	August, 1935	November, 1942
Rena R. Jenkins	Jan-July, 1922	April-Dec, 1937
Helen Church	January, 1938	January, 1944
May Sontag Schenck	October, 1939	March, 1946
Robert S. Clough	December, 1939	July, 1958
Marylee Holmes Hawkins	March, 1944	September, 1944
Cleta Null Rodgers	December, 1944	October, 1945
Dorothy Bacon Pepper	October, 1945	December, 1948
Virgil Burk	December, 1945	February, 1947
Shirley Pohlenz Drinkard	June, 1946	June, 1947
Lester O. Akers	October, 1946	To date
Charline Lindsay	July, 1947	To date
Eldon Williams	July, 1947	May, 1950
John Burkeholder	June, 1949	To date
Ruth Crowley Upchurch	January, 1950	February, 1954
Mary Dell McCain	June, 1950	June, 1957
Grant R. Shrum	July, 1953	November, 1954
Mrs. Marian Beebe	September, 1954	March, 1961
Arthur C. Ausherman	June, 1955	To date
Frank Graham	February, 1957	To date
Charity Bye Shank	November, 1957	August, 1958
Nelson Trickey	May, 1958	To date
George P. Rowe	November, 1958	To date
Bill Wickersham	June, 1962	To date
Virginia Norris	September, 1959	March, 1962
Jo Ellen McKay Meeker	August, 1961	July, 1962
Rebecca Williams Schnakenberg	October, 1962	August, 1963
Clemie Dunn	December, 1964	To date

Others, on appointment for short periods, included Roy Keller in 1917, Floris Hands in 1918, Florine Fate in 1920, Mrs. Frances D. Bridges in 1921, W. D. Wade in 1921, Albert Leonard in 1922.

MISSOURI IFYE ALUMNI

Year	Name	Home County	Host Country Abroad
1949	Van E. Eitel	Adair	Belgium
1950	Scott Sawyer, Jr.	Nodaway	France
1952	Mrs. Herbert G. Rich (Maribel Norris)	Knox	England-Wales
1952	Jack Whitesell	Cedar	Mexico
1952	John F. Gerber	Morgan	Switzerland
1953	Robert W. Shoemyer	Shelby	Netherlands
1953	Mrs. Hal Jenkins (Carolyn Vandiver)	Shelby	Israel
1953	Mrs. Claire Olsen (Carolyn E. Butt)	Atchison	Puerto Rico
1954	Clark E. Garner	Shelby	Equador
1954	Mrs. Ed Sheen (Shirley Yagel)	Linn	Finland
1954	Mrs. Chester Barton (Jo Ann Noble)	Buchanan	Scotland
1954	Helen McHugh	Vernon	Germany
1954	Silas Ray White	Newton	Ireland/N. Ireland
1954	Mrs. David Reed (Patricia Redhage)	Franklin	Chile
1955	Helen Lehenbauer	Marion	Austria
1955	Mrs. J. N. Smith (Patricia Wetherell)	Boone	Israel
1955	Thomas Pfitzner	Lawrence	England-Wales
1955	Robert A. Gibson	Holt	India
1956	Larry Dingus	St. Clair	France
1956	Homer Jarman	Johnson	Costa Rica
1956	Mrs. Charles Moreland (Marilyn Anderson)	Cass	India
1956	Jack Melton	Lawrence	Greece
1957	Mrs. Bill Dowler (Dorothea Drane)	Boone	Denmark
1957	William R. Waller	Buchanan	Uruguay
1957	Richard Taylor	Shelby	Switzerland
1957	Sister Mary Margaret (Mary M. Johanning)	Howard	Luxembourg
1957	Cleo Kottwitz	Maries	Brazil
1957	Rodney Garnett	Cole	Norway
1958	Mrs. Kenneth Gasper (Rosemary Weiss)	Cape Girardeau	Netherlands
1958	Mrs. John Gooch (Beth Hammond)	Grundy	Germany
1958	Jack Huff	Douglas	Netherlands
1958	David Hunter	Pike	Pakistan
1959	Matt Alexander	St. Clair	Turkey
1959	Mrs. Gerhard Clement (Sally Gladden)	Texas	Germany
1959	Robert Knoernschild	St. Charles	Japan
1960	Mrs. B. Hawkins (Glenda Rhoades)	Pettis	Sweden
1960	Edmund Bohl, Jr.	Gasconade	Australia
1960	Robert Fridley	St. Louis	Greece
1960	Mrs. Edgar Schnakenberg (Rebecca Williams)	Douglas	Argentina
1961	Tom Risch	Franklin	Israel
1961	Mrs. Anna Lou Hunziger (Anna Lou Karrasch)	Andrew	Netherlands
1961	Byron Rosbrugh	St. Clair	Switzerland
1961	Mrs. Wendell Frankenbach (Margorie Faeth)	St. Charles	Ireland/N. Ireland
1961	Mrs. Richard Becker (Nancy Ewing)	Vernon	England/Wales
1962	Mary Joan Temple	Lafayette	France
1962	Alice Ann Dyer (Mrs. Alice Hassler)	DeKalb	Finland
1962	Quinten Huss	Clinton	Brazil

IFYE ALUMNI (Cont'd.)

Year	Name	County	Host Country
1962	Robert McGill	Newton	Germany
1963	Betty Mae Easter	Mercer	Turkey
1963	John Gebhards	Atchison	Brazil
1963	Mrs. Farron M. Light (Farron Massey)	Laclede	Italy
1963	LeRoy Huff	Scotland	Ireland/N. Ireland
1964	John Crouch	Clay	Venezuela
1964	Margaret Cooper	Jackson	Luxembourg
1964	Robert Horton	Adair	New Zealand
1964	Robert Ferguson	Buchanan	Peru

IFYE GUESTS IN MISSOURI

Name-Home Address	Dates in Missouri	Family & County Visited
Mr. Claude Foucault Montreau-Mereville Seine Et Oise, France	May, 1949-Jan., 1950	Perry Ewing, Boone R. W. Walters, Johnson Thompson Ranch, Sullivan
Miss Pamela Sheppard Preston Cottage Iwerne Minster Blandford Dorset, England	Sep., 1950	C. T. Richards, Daviess
Mr. Hans Thude Vilslev Pr. Gredstedbro, Denmark	June 27-Aug. 18, 1952 (Left Program)	P. H. Emberson, Knox
Miss Gertrud Schori Uettligen, Ct. Bern Switzerland	Sep. 24-Dec. 10, 1952	Carl Rudolph, Andrew John Bechter, Andrew
Mr. Heiner Kiefhaber Katzweiler Krs. Kaiserlautern Land Rheinland-Pfalz, Germany	Sep. 25-Oct. 25, 1952	Virgil Goff, Worth
Miss Sara Zinkweg Middelsluis OZ 37 Numansdorp, Netherlands	Oct. 16, 1952-Jan. 3, 1953	Ben Donaldson, Laclede
Mr. Adolfo Glave Argentina	May 18-Aug. 23, 1953	Frank Nelson, Andrew Dale Clement, Nodaway
Mr. Paul Walshe Umutaoroa, R.D. Dannevirke Southern Hawkes Bay, New Zealand	May 26-Aug. 23, 1953	Hugh Pond, Howell Eric Heimsoth, Lafayette
Mr. Alexander Wilson Gartland Mains Lanark, Scotland	June 8-July 19, 1953	Flint McRoberts, Lewis
Mr. Kalle Saura Vanrikki Sttolinkatu IIc Helsinke, Finland	June 5-Sep. 8, 1953	J. S. Denslow, Adair Chester Cowan, Adair
Miss Carmen Burgos Corozal, Puerto Rico	June 5-July 27, 1953	Fitzhugh Diggs, Hamburg, Iowa
Mr. William Martin Tierkelly Balleyroney, Benbridge, County Down, North Ireland	July 15-Oct. 4, 1953	John Ferree, Jasper Guerney Greshan, Jasper Floyd Youngblood, Jasper
Miss Joan Playle Manor Farm Litlington, Cambridgeshire, England	Sept. 14-Oct. 17, 1953	C. G. Scott, New Madrid
Mr. David Guthrie Bank of Australia 6 Albermarle St., W.I., England	Oct. 13, 1953-Jan. 10, 1954	Joe Kirchdoerfer, Cape C. W. Henderson, Cape
Mr. Johann M. Christern 24b Oldenburg Holstein Georgenhof, Germany	Apr. 30-June 23, 1954	Harry Leubrecht, Pike John Bremer, Cass

Name-Home Address	Dates in Missouri	Family and County Visited
Miss Raija Nihtila Jarvela, Finland	Aug. 27-Sept. 30, 1954	Francis Waller, Buchanan
Mr. Leon Stassart 68 Rue de Fleures Mellet, Belgium	July 15-Sept. 3, 1954	W. P. Boyer, Scotland Paul Schenks, Scotland
Mr. Mahmoud S. Gadalla 30 Ubn Khaldoun St., Cairo, Egypt	Oct. 15, 1954-Jan. 5, 1955	Wayne Dernier, Boone Earl Mudd, Monroe
Miss Alaide Cabrera LaSierra, Maldonado Uruguay	Oct. 18, 1954-Jan. 10, 1955	Fred Kipp, Morgan Allen Foreman, Marion Fay Warden, Worth Virgil Goff, Worth
Mr. Angel Lopez Rojas Rinconada de Los Andes Aconcagua, Chili	Aug. 31, 1954-Jan. 10, 1955	Harold Baile, Johnson Jennings Clonts, Johnson Newton Teegardin, Caldwell Gordon Thompson, DeKalb Clifford Duce, DeKalb John Baker, DeKalb W. E. Brewer, Linn
Mr. Fernando Mora Palmares, Costa Rica	May 30-Aug. 24, 1954	John Williams, Grundy Ed Weaver, Oregon
Mr. Yoseph Levi Beth - Hanan, Israel	Mar. 30-June 11, 1954	V. B. Vandiver, Shelby Joseph Sanning, Cole
Mr. Nicholas Milios Calameta, Greece	July 21-Sep. 20, 1954	Glen Shields, Carroll J. E. Winslow, Adair
Miss Myra Hugill Prospect Hill Catterick Yorks, England	Aug. 30-Oct. 4, 1954	Harold McCarty, Callaway
Miss Viola Nilsson Box 303 Nordmaling, Sweden	May 13-Aug. 17, 1954	Oscar Thorne, Linn Ed Marquardt, Vernon Milan Berry, Lawrence
Mr. Geoffrey Dixon Borwick's Aynsome Cartmel Grange Over Sands Lancashire, England	June 21-Aug. 17, 1955	Dan Gates, Harrison George Seiberling, Livingston C. O. Surber, Livingston
Miss Carmen Rodriquez Parcela No. 41 Colonia Pedro Aguirre Cerda Malloa, Chile	June 15-Aug. 15, 1955	Edwin Redhage, Franklin John Cummings, Gentry
Miss Terttu Kolemainen Kasarminkatu 11 a.15 Kuopio, Finland	Aug. 10-Nov. 7, 1955	Clifton Winfrey, Carrol Elvin Schroeder, Atchison
Mr. Robert Fort Domaine'de Caunette Basse Par Moussouleus Aude, France	June 14-Aug. 26, 1955	Warren Gibson, Holt Eugene Carl, Lawrence E. H. Melton, Lawrence
Mr. Josy Hein Wasserbillig, Luxembourg	May 25-Aug. 10 1955	Phillip Dingus, St. Clair Carney James, Maries

Name—Home Address	Dates in Missouri	Family and County Visited
Miss Atiya Sultana Rafat Kada Barket Pura, Hyderabad Deccan, India	Aug. 29–Nov. 8, 1955	Lewis Kirtz, Holt Herschel Crawford, Macon L. B. Smith, Jackson
Miss Kirubarathy Cross 5 Ribeiro St., Rayape Hah Madras 14, India	Aug. 29–Nov. 8, 1955	Cecil Davis, Harrison Wm. Marsh, Macon Harold Rugen, Pettis
Mr. George Perler c/o Dominik Perler Wunnewill Canton Fribourg, Switzerland	May 14–July 30, 1956	Charles William, Douglas E. Y. Crouch, Clay Loren Cullum, Putnam
Mr. Cemal Demir Kacaafsar Kcyu Balya Balikesir, Turkey	June 2–July 30, 1956	Walter Brazeale, Christian W. B. Schaefer, Osage
Mr. Demetrios Spyridakis Petrokephali Heracklion Crete, Greece	June 6–July 30, 1956	Wm. Steinhouser, Jackson Wm. Bohnert, Jackson Louis Wade, Newton Earl Clement, Newton
Miss Charlotte Snaith Leaps Rigg, Walton Brampton Cumberland, England	Aug. 7–Sept. 1, 1956	Richard McDaniel, Stoddard
Miss Marlene Rix Gross-Buchwalduber Neumunster Schleswig-Holstein, Germany	June 25–Sept. 21, 1956	Wilfred Mitchener, Saline Mrs. Paul Lehenbauer, Marion Wm. Boettcher, Gasconade
Mr. R. P. Bhatnagar Rose View, Khairnager Gate Meerut City Uttar Pradesh, India	Aug. 5–Oct. 28, 1956	Wilbur Gates, Daviess Donald Real, Daviess E. A. Mooney, Jefferson Floyd Valle, Jefferson John McBee, Caldwell
Mr. K. N. Deshmukh Ramkrisna-Niwas Amravati Camp Madhya Predesh, India	Aug. 5–Oct. 28, 1956	A. Knorenschild, St. Charles Virgil Shirley, Ray George Myers, Mercer
Mr. G. R. Manuel c/o Dr. P. Manuel 2 High School Road Tanjore Dist. Porayar P.O. 3 Madras State, India	Aug. 5–Oct. 28, 1956	Walter Heid, Cass Charles McLarney, Clinton Robert Thompson, Greene
Mr. Athanel Da Fonseca Rua Santo Afonso- 113 Rio de Janeiro Brazil	Aug. 5–Nov. 11, 1956	Norris West, Platte Arlo Cottrell, Platte Leo Archer, Nodaway T. H. Thorne, Linn
Mr. Moshe Margalit Giuat-Ada, Israel	Sept. 24–Nov. 29, 1956	Rev. Gene Wetherell, Boone R. M. Again, Boone J. C. Bennett, Gentry

Name—Home Address	Dates in Missouri	Family and County Visited
Mr. Reza Saeb Pahlavi Hospital, Oulia St. Daraii's House, Tehran, Iran	Apr. 26–July 27, 1957	Lesley England, Audrain Mrs. Agnes Yoest, Moniteau Marvin Collier, Carroll
Mr. Carlos Harley San Joaquin de Flores Heredia, Costa Rica	May 13–Aug. 4, 1957	Richard Cantwell, Mississippi A. E. Hammond, Grundy Chas. Wintermute, Nodaway
Mr. Mahmoud Hamid Shaqlawa, Iraq	April 26–July 27, 1957	Thos. Glendining, Ralls Gilbert Jestes, Dekalb Rienhardt Riekhof, Lafayette
Mr. Andres De. La Torre, Jr. Calle Central No. 3470 La Concepcion Provincia de Ciriqui, Panama	May 10–Aug. 4, 1957	Paul McLain, Harrison F. J. Fallert, St. Genevieve Noel Elliot, Douglas
Miss Jennifer Altham 10 Grange Road Bushey, Herts, England	May 20–Aug. 4, 1957	Jewell Jeffries, Livingston Maurice Robbins, Newton Philip Lampkin, Henry Earl Clements, Newton
Mr. George Henry Magheragall Lisburn, Co. Antrim, Northern Ireland	June 29–Aug. 4, 1957	Roy Long, Chariton W. H. Watkins, Pemiscot
Miss Lidia Estevez Solis de Mataojo Dpt. de Lavalleja R. O. del Uruguay	May 10–Aug. 4, 1957	Paul Kroner, Randolph Earl Snyder, Lawrence Laurence Litchey, Lawrence Dayton Pauley, Putnam
Miss E. Britt Jonsson Klefstad Askeby, Sweden	Aug. 12–Oct. 26, 1957	Wm. Boxley, Mercer Wm. Diechman, Montgomery W. T. Gassner, Gentry
Miss Ingeborg Lervang Fylkeshuset Drammen, Norway	Aug. 13–Nov. 25, 1957	Fred Garnett, Cole James Harness, Lincoln Harold Krieg, Shelby Harold Roth, Cass
Mr. Alfonso Mena Durini Calle Cordero 1495 Quito, Ecuador	Sept. 13–Nov. 6, 1957	Flint McRoberts, Lewis Marvin Forkner, Vernon Wm. Ledgerwood, Oregon
Mr. Norbert Lefebvre Celles, Rue Du Moulin 17 Belgium	Aug. 12–Sept. 15, 1957	Olin Guest, Andrew
Miss Francine Cornaille Ferme d'Iris Clary (Nord) France	June 28–Sept. 14, 1957	John Washburn, Linn Roy Hilty, St. Clair Forest Widel, Cooper
Mr. Pekka Pastila Torittu Padasjoki, Finland	May 30–July 27, 1958	Wesley Schulze, Warren Clark Noel, Putnam
Mr. Demetrios Biris 45 Nikiforou Lytra Street Athens, Greece	June 21–Sept. 6, 1958	Harry T. Bray, Johnson John McClanahan, Pemiscot Jerome Sanders, Randolph Clarence Powell, Randolph

Name—Home Address	Dates in Missouri	Family and County Visited
Mr. Aftab Shahban Shahban Road Shikarpur, West Pakistan	Aug. 4–Oct. 19, 1958	Delbert Barton, Buchanan Ira Bodenhausen, Buchanan Robert Thomson, Greene Epperson Jerome, Henry
Mr. Aftabur Rahman P. O. Bhola, District Barisal East Pakistan	Aug. 4–Oct. 19, 1958	Raymond Tieman, Lafayette Allen Rankin, Douglas Clifton Morrison, Bates
Miss Maggy Biren Merl, Luxembourg	Aug. 4–Oct. 31, 1958	Bernard Joahanning, Howard Ray Bennett, Scott Fritz Leitman, Lincoln Ray Creason, Carroll
Mr. Alejandro Rodriquez 50v al Este del Mercado San Ramon, Costa Rica	Aug. 3–Oct. 9, 1958	Bill Schauer, Livingston Laurence Arthaud, Livingston Alfred Beckmeyer, Boone Walter Peterson, Audrain
Mr. Ramon Espinosa Garcia Jorge Juan 78 4 Madrid, Spain	Sept. 26–Nov. 7, 1958	William Ficek, Grundy Lester Lutes, Worth
Miss Martina A. Oele Suezkade 110 The Hague, Netherlands	June 9–July 26, 1959	Lloyd Miller, Dunklin C. Goldsberry, Texas
Mr. Gunnar Anderson Valla Gard Linkoping, Sweden	May 19–July 26, 1959	John Karrasch, Andrew Harold Jones, Miller Emmet Wood, Shelby
Miss Margarida Fontes Emilio, Jardin Square, 51 Vicosa, Minas, Gerais, Brazil	April 29–July 26, 1959	Cletus Comte, St. Francis Will Daldrup, Henry John Berry, Lawrence Thine McClurg, Lawrence
Miss Lucia Nogueira Casilla 73 Rengo, Chile	Aug. 2–Oct. 8, 1959	Wallace Boyer, Scott Hugh Alexander, Moniteau Glenn Chappell, Sullivan
Miss Anna–Marie Harmeyer Westerkappeln, Lada 28 Post Velpe/Westf., Germany	Aug. 2–Nov. 7, 1959	Victor Martin, Jefferson Chas. Grebing, Perry Gene Selvey, Barton Dean Thomas, Barton
Mr. Louis Htin Aung No. 51 Block 8 Zigon Upper Burma	May 27–July 18, 1959	Gordon Saunders, Dekalb Herman Rosbrugh, St. Clair
Mr. Stephen Bawk Naw c/o Saya U.M. Matu, Momouk, Kachin State, Bhamo, Burma	May 27–July 18, 1959	Frank Bonderer, Livingston Wm. Braun, Johnson Frank Boruschski, Newton
Mr. Jean Godart Champigneville Dept. Ardennes, France	Aug. 2–Oct. 26, 1959	John Ricketts, Iron Thad Gaston, Clark Glenn Tharp, Putnam
Mr. Mario M. Lopez Avenida Bartolome Mitre 568, Carmen de Areco, Buenos Aires, Argentina	Aug. 2–Oct. 8, 1959	Cloyce Wilson, Pettis Sam Crook, Ray George Barnitz, Dent

Name–Home Address	Dates in Missouri	Family and County Visited
Mr. Pierre Savary Rue de la Bergeris 31 Payern (Vaud) Switzerland	May 24–July 25, 1960	Roy Jackson, Macon A. Vogelsmeier, Carroll E. S. Gladden, Texas
Miss Kazue Iwaski 604, Miyakami Shimizu City Shizuoka Pref., Japan	July 31–Sept. 28, 1960	Leonard Doll, Bates John Cruce, Bates L. B. Edwards, Callaway R. Knoernschild, St. Charles Wm. Brengarth, Cooper Harold Jones, Miller
Mr. Alfred G. Walker "Cloverlea" Victor Harbour So. Australia, Australia	July 2–July 24, 1960	E. A. Bohl, Gasconade Harve Ferguson, Buchanan Ben Parnell, Taney Olin Wolf, Taney
Miss Fiona E. Ellis Fruitvale, Aughagallon Lurgan, County Armagh, N. Ireland	July 31–Aug. 11, 1960	Harold Goff, Worth Flint McRoberts, Lewis
Mr. Chen-Lung Hsieh 26, Chang Shi Rd. Fan-po Li, Chi-Fu Changwa, Hsien, Taiwan (Rep. of China)	July 31–Sept. 28, 1960	J. W. Gagnepain, Perry Howard Jaynes, Ralls Chester Rohr, Ralls D. L. Hertzog, Jackson
Mr. Pantouses Kaltsikes Nigrita, Greece; School Address: 54 Tsimski St. Salonika, Greece	May 30–July 25, 1960	Robert Smith, St. Louis Marvin Fridley, St. Louis Gene Montgomery, St. Louis Leonard Cox, Caldwell C. W. Begey, Newton
Mr. Leon G. Gasataya Blummentritt St., Guimbal, Iloilo, Philippines	July 31–Sept. 28, 1960	Howard Bier, Marion Herbert Vogel, Franklin Robert Hartley, Boone
Mr. Mathias J. Gjone Gjnnes, Hedrum Pr Larvik, Norway	Aug. 3–Nov. 5, 1961	Alvis Applebury, Livingston Norbert Schwerman, Montgomery Tom Amos, Bates Rex DeShon, Sr., Buchanan
Miss Mary Alice Bickley Aller Barton, Sandford, Credition, Devon, England	July 31–Sept. 14, 1961	Marvin Forkner, Vernon Wm. C. Brown, Ralls Thos. Bailey, Jackson
Miss Graziella Baldi Ospedaletta (Trento) Italy	May 18–July 24, 1961	Wm. Brengarth, Cooper Chas. McLarney, Clinton Jerry Huggins, Barton Leland Breedlove, Laclede
Mr. Atilio Garibaldi M. Calle "Grau" N406 Chincha Alta, Peru	May 26–July 23, 1961	L. E. Clark, Boone Frank Welch, Nodaway Neil Perberton, Stone
Mr. Edward Bradley Ballycoolan, Stradvally Portlaois, Laois, Ireland	June 4–July 23, 1961	C. Collins, Christian Robt. Shipley, Sullivan
Mr. Celal Kargili Sofular Mah., Sokak 30 ev 30, Tarsus, Turkey	July 31–Nov. 6, 1961	Henry Boessen, Cole LeRoy Bowman, DeKalb Robt. Thompson, Greene

Name—Home Address	Dates in Missouri	Family and County Visited
Miss Juana Malo T. Casilla Postal 235 Cuenca, Ecuador	July 31–Nov. 7, 1961	Merwyan Howard, Lawrence James Justus, Platte Wayne Brown, Franklin Irvin S teiger, Franklin E. P. Montgomery, St. Louis
Mr. Paul J. Franken Moeangiangi Station P. Bag, Napier, New Zealand	Aug. 7–Sept., 1962	Arthur James, Monroe Milton Miller, Buchanan
Miss Margarita Muriel Q. Sopetran Antioquia, Colombia	Aug. 6–Oct. 9, 1962	Frank Cobb, Montgomery Latimer Jones, Livingston Emmett Jackson, Ralls
Miss Ofra Amir Beit Shearim (Moshav), Israel	Aug. 6–Oct. 29, 1962	Maurice Robbins, Newton Stanley Hedges, Johnson Sam Mundy, Audrain Milton Krueger, Clark
Mr. D. J. Patel Ratanpura, P.O., Palitana Bhawanagar, Gujerat State, India	June 10–July 29, 1962	Virgil Koch, Boone Ray Plank, Sullivan Alfred Hahn, St. Louis
Miss Mary C. Miller Arnish, Witchburn Rd. Cambeltow, Arygll, Scotland	June 3–July 29, 1962	Walter Faith, St. Charles Mrs. Arthur Huff, Scott
Mr. Bengt Wallgren Bista, Langhundra, Sweden	May 31–July 29, 1962	Ervin Hedeman, Dade Ray Wolf, Atchison Glen Rhoads, Pettis
Mr. Basu Dev Parajuli Pokhara, Miruwa, West No. 3, Nepal	May 31–July 22, 1962	LeRoy Brown, DeKalb K. W. Gunnels, Bates
Mr. Jacob Sypkens 38 Ommelanderweg Kloosterburen, Netherlands	May 31–July 29, 1962	Flint McRoberts, Lewis Chas. Weaver, Jasper Bob McMillan, Laclede
Mr. Pedro Manuel Fernandez Los Pantanos, Bocone, (Estado Trujillo, Venezuela En el Caserio de la Placita)	Aug. 6–Oct. 9, 1962	H. Gay Franks, Benton G. Whittinghill, Pulaski Wesley Doughty, Daviess Albert Trimble, Daviess Ernest Knapp, Daviess George Smith, Daviess Ralph Langford, Daviess
Miss Leena Rai Suntala Ghari, Illam, Nepal	June 12–July 20, 1962	Calvin Schweizer, Andrew Mrs. J. W. Brown, Clinton
Mr. Mohammed Zoha P.O. Gaibandha Dist. Rhagpur, E. Pakistan	June 14–Aug. 3, 1963	Truman Olbricht, Oregon Norman Casper, Barry Harry Planchian, Barry G. Wittinghill, Pulaski
Miss Marcelle Bronzon LaRosiere, LeMontSur Lausanne V. D., Switzerland	Aug 12–Oct. 20, 1963	Glen Posler, Harrison W. J. Wiley, Stone Larry Estep, Clinton

Name–Home Address	Dates in Missouri	Family and County Visited
Mr. Engin Gazileri 19 Mayis Mahallisi Bahariye Caddesi 27 Samsun, Turkey	Aug. 12–Nov. 5, 1963	Alfred Hahn, St. Louis Norman Irons, Livingston Tommy Call, Daviess Grimes Spillman, Daviess Clyde Brown, Ralls
Miss Marthe Lemaitre La Cheralleri, Mehaudin Cauterne Orne, France	Aug. 12–Oct. 19, 1963	David Andrews, Dunklin Richard Moore, Howell James Collier, Laclede
Mr. Horst Bretschneidier Los Ceirillos Canelanes, Uruguay	May 9–Aug. 3, 1963	George Russell, Boone Bernard Brown, Gasconade Fred Bodenhamer, Andrew Lester Rottman, Warren
Mr. Beresford Forbes Chester Castle P.O. Hanover, Jamaico, W.I.	June 7–July 25, 1963	Roy Cooper, Sr., Pemiscot John West, Pemiscot Olie Sallee, Boone Walter Harris, Jr., Boone
Mr. Peter Saverimuttu Group 7 – Kanagapuram Kilincochchi, Ceylon	June 6–Aug. 3, 1963	Harold Foss, Linn Erwin Hedeman, Dade George Mehan, Pettis
Miss Marina Ronceros Jiron Los Angles No 396 Chincha Alla, Lima Peru	May 27–Aug. 3, 1963	Ted Owens, Newton Wm. Waller, Buchanan Lester Lankford, Newton Fred Huhman, Miller
Miss Alma Baumgarten 6411 Ritzelshof Post, Reid/Fulda, Germany	Aug. 12–Oct. 19, 1963	Robert Shipley, Sullivan Oscar Wiechert, Chariton H. A. Vaughan, Jefferson
Mr. Chhaburao Avad Post Jeur Kumbhari, Tal Kopargaon Dist. Ahmednagar Maharashtra State, India	Aug. 19–Oct. 21, 1964	Ray Shull, Jasper Jack Palmer, Callaway Peter Myers, New Madrid Nelson Gruen, New Madrid
Mr. Ramon Albeiro Pereira Finca "San Ramon," Chiguara Merida, Venezuela	Aug. 10–Oct. 17, 1964	Howard Lock, Osage Arlen Watson, Boone Flint McRoberts, Lewis
Mr. Hermann Felber Kemating 34, P. Oberndorf Salzburg, Austria	Aug. 10–Oct. 10, 1964	Raymond Wade, Greene Frank Cobb, Montgomery Alfred Kaup, Stone
Miss Gunbritt Ekstrom Rasegarden Hasslosa Vinnings, Sweden	Aug. 10–Nov. 27, 1964	Sam McKenzie, Knox Harley Almond, Sullivan John Shonkwiler, Newton Joe Austin, Newton G. Wesselschmidt, Franklin Lewis Ferrell, Iron
Miss Antoinette Reuter 14 rue Fr. J. Vannerus Diekirch, Grand-Duche of Luxembourg	May 29–Aug. 2, 1964	Arlie Wetzel, Livingston Erwin Hedeman, Dade Don White, Jackson Alva Clark, Jackson

Miss Iaraci Piazera Dippold
Rue Rafael Pardinho
159 San Francisco
Do Sul, Santa Catarina, Brazil

May 6-July 29, 1964

Dr. H. Thurman, Platte
Grimes Spillman, Daviess
Elwood Hackler, Miller
Joe Jones, Dunklin

Mr. Michele Palazzo
Via S. Francesco 77
Castellaneta (Taranto) Italy

May 20-Aug. 2, 1964

Emmett Lewton, Ralls
Lee Welliver, Bates
Early Todd, Lawrence
Herbert Hadlock, Lawrence

Mr. Dong-Ho Shur
No 187, So-Ko Ri,
Mo-Ka Myon
Ichon, Gun, Kyongi, Korea

May 27-July 29, 1964

Warren Crider, Holt
M. H. Colley, Putnam
Wm. Fortner, Clinton

DELEGATES TO NATIONAL 4-H CLUB CONFERENCE

(1927 – 1964)

Year	Name	County	Address*
1927	Albert Dyer	DeKalb	Queen Ann Dr., Columbia, Mo.
	Mrs. E. S. Turner, Jr. (Nellie Mabel Jones)		
		Buchanan	Rt. 3, St. Joseph, Mo.
	Mrs. Kenneth K. Cokely (Elsa Gibson)		
		Caldwell	608 College Liberty, Mo.
	Roy Nicholson (M.D.)	Ray	312 Columbia Pike, Arlington, Va.
1928	Mrs. Charles F. Lane (Amelia Dunn)		
		Buchanan	R. 2, Box 245, Lutz, Fla.
	Lutie T. Chiles	Jackson	478 Mills St., Liberty, Mo.
	Wayne Short	St. Charles	Cocoanut Grove, Fla.
	Herbert Fick	St. Louis	143 Huntleigh, Kirkwood 22, Mo.
1929	Orin Cletus Swackhammer	Henry	R. 3, Tarkio, Mo.
	Billy Winfrey	Jackson	830 Cambridge, Topeka, Kans.
	Mrs. Elman Morrow (Lorine Hostetter)		
		Jackson	Sibley, Mo.
	Mrs. Fred Benge (Lola Acklin)		
		Nodaway	Graham, Mo.
1930	Mrs. Loren Washburn (Anita Zagrodsky)		
		Buchanan	Versailles, Mo.
	J. B. McCorkle	Howard	R. 20, Kansas City, Mo.
	Mrs. A. W. Maxwell (Marguerite Ferguson)		
		Jackson	Lee's Summit, Mo.
	Elwood Motte	St. Louis	Nashville 23, Mo.
1931	Mrs. Merle Webb (Regina Kneib)		
		Buchanan	Chico, Calif.
	Mrs. Fred Paulsmeyer (Kathryn Davis)		
		Lincoln	Silex, Mo.
	Raymond Richmond	Linn	Laclede, Mo.
	Harry Beatty	Oregon	Drumright, Okla.
1932	E. C. Adams, Jr.	Jackson	5425 Easton, St. Louis, Mo.
	Harold Thieman	Lafayette	Concordia, Mo.
	Mary Elizabeth Triplett	Lafayette	Washington, 9, D.C. (F.B.I. Office)
	Mrs. Art Pollman (Floreine Brown)		
		Lincoln	Silex, Mo.
1933	Mrs. Carl Schudde (Bernice Zagrodsky)		
		Buchanan	221 N. Florissant Rd., Ferguson, Mo.
	Mrs. Durbette Kubick (Zelma B. Whiteside)		
		Greene	827 Reddock, Memphis, Tenn.
	Roy Lentz	Jackson	7425 Maywood, Raytown, Mo.
	Kenneth Guyer	Linn	Purdin, Mo.
1934	Mrs. Wm. M. Hawkins (Mary Lee Holmes)		1125 Michele Way, Santa Rose,
		Buchanan	California
	Frank B. Milne	Holt	Oregon, Mo.
	Fred J. Brune	Jackson	Buckner, Mo.
	Mrs. Calvin Shrout (Mildred E. Ayres)		
		Lafayette	Oak Grove, Mo.
1935	Harry Broermann	Atchison	R. 3 Tarkio, Mo.
	Mrs. Ralph Gallagher (Frieda Kneib)		
		Buchanan	Maryville, Mo.
	Mrs. Lawrence Spier (Opal Caldwell)		
		Cass	Cleveland, Mo.
	Ervin Brune	Jackson	Chanute, Kans.

* The addresses given are correct as recorded in the Extension Office, University
Missouri – Columbia, January 1, 1965.

1936	J. Alton Riffle	Cass	Box 1055, Kansas City 41, Mo.
	Mary Ida Sullivan	Jackson	124 E. Lindon, Independence, Mo.
	Mrs. Robt. M. Meyer (Betty Hefferman)		
		Pettis	Rockville, Conn.
	C.L. Buoy (Deceased)	Howard	Killed in World War II
1937	Mrs. Arthur Frank (Lila Lee Conrad)		
		Buchanan	1405 S. 39th St. Joseph, Mo.
	Joe E. Edmondson	Greene	R. Columbia, Mo.
	Ray L. Milne	Holt	Prosner, Wash.
	Mrs. Raymond A. Schroeder (Neva McCracken)		
		Newton	2019 Country Club Dr., Columbia, Mo.
1938	Mrs. Orville Lewis (Marjorie Mae Smith)		
		Howard	1500 Providence Rd., Columbia, Mo.
	James F. Milton	Jackson	Independence, Mo.
	Denzil B. Sigars	Jasper	107 E. 18th St., Higginsville, Mo.
	Mrs. Waunita Sanders (Waunita Cantwell)		
		Lawrence	Miller, Mo.
1939	Mrs. Thomas C. White (Bernice Hitzemann)		
		Carroll	Norborne, Mo.
	Mrs. Clayton Peterman (Mary L. Johnston)		
		Jasper	Miami, Mo.
	Howard Broemelsick	St. Louis	Memphis, Tenn.
	Dwight Brassfield	Grundy	R. 7, Trenton, Mo.
1940	Mrs. Harry Riehl (Naomi M. Lentz)		
		Boone	Potosi, Mo.
	Harold H. Grothoff	Cole	St. Louis, Mo.
	Mrs. Gray W. Miller (Jean Agnes Norbury)		
		Greene	Baltimore, 3, Md.
	Wayne E. Buswell	Linn	Lovington, N.M.
1941	Mrs. Alva Clark (Mary Jean Lentz		Jackson
		Jackson	Independence, Mo.
	Jack McFerron	Jasper	Memphis, Tenn.
	Jim C. Heitmeyer	Monroe	Carrollton, Mo.
	Mrs. Vernon Rinehart (Marceline Lankford)		
		Newton	Seneca, Mo., R. 1
1946	Mrs. Frankie Botts (Frankie McLean		
		Greene	804 Maplewood, Columbia, Mo.
	Harry Edwards	Moniteau	4407 Vermont, Kansas City, Mo.
	Herbert E. Clizer	Andrew	R. 1, Savannah, Mo.
	Mrs. Ray H. Faes (Rejeana Daniel)		
		Shelby	Brunswick, Mo.
1947	Richard Larson	Jasper	Carl Junction, Mo.
	Mrs. Roger Hecht (Amy Virginia Pearl)		
		Osage	3010 Arnold Court, Topeka, Kans.
	Rolla J. Plattner	Saline	Grand Pass, Mo.
	Mrs. J. V. Worstell (Laura Frances Davis)		
		Harrison	Mexico, Mo.
1948	Wayne Gerber	Andrew	Skidmore, Mo.
	Mrs. Leon Welburn (Stella Sperber)		
		Pettis	Green Ridge, Mo.
	Robert L. Norris	Putnam	Unionville, Mo.
	Mrs. Gene D. Harsh (Shirley Peterman)		
		Saline	122 Thomas Rd., McMurrage, Pa.
1949	Mrs. Frank Moser (Dorothea McCue)		Andrew
		Andrew	Rt. 2, Savannah, Mo.
	James T. Davis	Harrison	508 Baker St., Monroe, La.
	Mrs. Louise Maddin	Nodaway	Florissant, Mo.
	Don Rutter	Shelby	3225 S. 118 St., Omaha, Nebr.

1950   Mrs. John A. Ficken (Jenna Lee Martin)
                Benton   Windson, Mo.
       Mrs. Dale Alexander (Frances Ann Richards)
                Daviess   Jameson, Mo.
       Frank A. Stanley   New Madrid   R. 1, Matthews, Mo.
       Emmett Fairfax   Pettis   Sedalia, Mo.

1951   Mrs. Max Oliver (Marjorie Nold)
                Andrew   Montgomery City, Mo.
       John A. Ficken   Benton   Windsor, Mo. RR
       T. Nelson Travis   Jackson   342 S. Englewood Ave.,
                                   Inglewood, Calif. 11
       Mrs. Hal Jenkins (Carolyn Vandiver) 116 W. Palm Croft, Tempe, Ariz.
                Shelby

1952   Richard De Shon   Buchanan   1118 N. 24th St., St. Joseph, Mo.
       Jack Whitesell   Cedar   6825 N. Rosemond, San Gabriel, Colo.
       Mrs. Wm. T. Gressley, Jr. (Norma Jo Peterman)
                Saline   Bolckow, Mo.
       Helen McHugh   Vernon   1901 Hopi Trail, Austin 3, Tex.

1953   Mrs. Darrell Waisner (Barbara Glenn)
                Benton   Box 384, Melvain, Iowa
       Duane Shingleton   Cass   Columbia, Mo.
       Richard Cummins   Gentry   Stanberry, Mo.
       Mrs. Edwin Sheen (Shirley Yagel)
                Linn   602 Blue, Richland, Wash.

1954   Mrs. Ralph Anderson (LaVeta Ann Phillips)
                Boone   2021 Lakeview Ave., Middleton, Wis.
       Konrad L. Heid   Cass   Princeton, Mo.
       Marilyn Brougher, Deceased
                Lawrence   ---
       Cecil M. Jr. (Junior Boyer)
                Scotland   3724 Greenwich, Independence, Mo.

1955   Mrs. Charles Moreland (Marilyn Marsh)
                Macon   Atlanta, Mo.
       Marilyn Anderson   Cass   Rt. 2, Harrisonville, Mo.
       David Peterman   Saline   Miami, Mo.
       Sterling Evans   Nodaway   6522 78th Terrace, Overland Park,
                                     Kans.

1956   Rodney Garnett   Cole   Centertown, Mo.
       Mrs. Gerald Zumbrunnen (Martha Ann Davis)
                Harrison   Clinton, Mo.
       Joe Stewart   Johnson   Farmington, Mo.
       Mrs. John Horn (Juanita Snider)
                Platte   R. 22, Kansas City 53, Mo.

1957   Marian Scott   Jasper   209A W. 3rd, Hermann, Mo.
       Mrs. H.M. Townley (Norma Jean Purdun)
                Daviess   Gilman City, Mo.
       Byron Simpson   Clinton   Egerton, Mo.
       Billy Joe West   Platte   R. 28, Kansas City, 54, Mo.

1958   Bob Teegarden   Caldwell   Gallatin, Mo.
       Mrs. Raymond Cowell (Katherine Lacy)
                Henry   Urich, Mo.
       Elizabeth Novinger Lawler Adair   1530 N. Coast Hgwy., Laguna
                                     Beach, Calif.
       Larry Rosenbaum   Nodaway   Graham, Mo.

1959   Mrs. Ed. Schnakenberg (Rebecca Williams)
                Douglas   Cole Camp, Mo.
       Elizabeth Moore   Shelby   Rt. 2, Bethel, Mo.
       Edwin Turner   Buchanan   R. 3, St. Joseph, Mo.
       Gary Clarkson   Macon   R. 2, LaPlata, Mo.

1960	Joan Temple	Lafayette	R. 1, Higginsville, Mo.
	Mrs. Harlan Borman (Judy Atkinson)		
		Calloway	McCredie, Mo.
	John A. Jones	Macon	Vandalia, Mo.
	Keith E. Julian	Greene	1552 Orange, El Centro, Calif.
1961	Mrs. Jas. W. Prather (Patsy Mathew)		
		Benton	835 E. 21st Ave., No. Kans. City, Mo.
	Jewell Frownefelter	Jasper	R. 3, Joplin, Mo.
	John Crouch	Clay	R. 21, Kansas City, Mo.
	Quinten Huss (Deceased)	Clinton	---
1962	Mrs. Benson Riley (Inalee Vogelsmeier)		
		Carroll	R. 1, Walnut Hill, Columbia, Mo.
	Joyce Brengarth	Cooper	R. 3, Boonville, Mo.
	Edward Lee Nierman	Lafayette	R. 3, Concordia, Mo.
	James Richard Roth	New Madrid	R. 1, Malden, Mo.
1963	Joan Turner	Buchanan	R. 3, St. Joseph, Mo.
	Evelyn Heath	Randolph	Box 31 , Clark, Mo.
	Harold Storck	Barry	Purdy, Mo.
	Larence Meyer	Nodaway	Maryville, R. 1, Mo.
1964	Leon McIntyre	Nodaway	R. 2, Burlington Jct., Mo.
	Steve Mills	Newton	R. 5, Neosho, Mo.
	Marsha Ann Nicholson	Shelby	R. 3, Shelbyville, Mo.
	Patticia Minks	Franklin	R. 2, Union, Mo.

MISSOURI DELEGATES TO REGIONAL 4-H CLUB CAMPS

Year

1948	Southern University, Baton Rouge, La.	Gertrude M. Hurd	Pemiscot
		Permelia Powell	Pemiscot
		Charles Davis	Pemiscot
		Timothy Welch	Dunklin
1949	A&I College, Nashville, Tenn.	Charles Wilson	Pemiscot
		Fred Braswell	Pemiscot
		Alma Welch	Pemiscot
		Mary Bradford	Mississippi
1950	Virginia State, Petersburg, Va.	James E. Kaufman	Pemiscot
		George W. Enlow	New Madrid
		James E. Brown	Mississippi
		Bertha Petty	New Madrid
1951	Agriculture, Mechanical, and Normal College, Pine Bluff, Ark.	David Humes	Pemiscot
		Murphy D. Myles	Mississippi
		Joe Reeves	Stoddard
		Guida Joyce Jackson	Scott
1952	Tuskegge Institute, Tuskegee, Ala.	George Wesley, Jr.	Pemiscot
		Johnny McWilliams	New Madrid
		Mildred Hawkins	Dunklin
		Annie Irene Higgins	Pemiscot
1953	Kentucky State College, Frankfort, Ky.	Otha L. Robinson	Stoddard
		Carl Fordson	Pemiscot
		Dorothy J. Fultz	Pemiscot
		Frances A. Eulinburg	New Madrid
1954	Jackson State College, Jackson, Miss.	Arlie Bea Turner	Dunklin
		Vara Lee Shoffner	New Madrid
		Joe Maddox	Pemiscot
1955	Howard University, Washington, D.C. (as in following years)	James E. Warfield	Scott
		Robert R. Ellis	New Madrid
		Senora Lee Walls	Pemiscot
		Elnora Jones	Pemiscot
1956	''	Jimmie Reese	Pemiscot
		Joe Eddie Steele	Pemiscot
		Flora Lee Wilson	Pemiscot
		Claudette McWilliams	New Madrid
1957	''	Eddie Lee Reed, Jr.	Pemiscot
		Joe George Mitchel	Pemiscot
		Denzzy Vernell Folson	Dunklin
		Joyce Hill	Pemiscot
1958	''	David Gladney	Mississippi
		Federick Flowers	New Madrid
		Pearl Vivian Townes	Pemiscot
		Inez Thompson	Pemiscot
1959	''	Robert E. Artis	Pemiscot
		Charles McWilliams	New Madrid
		Velma Lee Trainor	Dunklin
		Mae Alice Tucker	Scott

1960	''	Georgia Lee Nicholson	Scott
		Willie A. Wilson, Jr.	Pemiscot
		Mable Christine Jones	Dunklin
		Alice Arether Marks	Stoddard
1961	''	Theodore Andrews	Scott
		Kenso Nicholson	Scott
		Fleeta M. Battle	Pemiscot
		Pearlie M. Watson	Scott

1964 SUMMARY OF NATIONAL 4-H AWARDS

Awards Program	Donor	County	State	Sectional	National
1. Achievement	Ford Motor Co. Fund, Dearborn, Mich.	4 gold-filled medals of honor	Trip to National 4-H Club Congress	None	12 scholarships of $500 each. Silver trays to 1st place boy/girl
2. Agricultural	International Harvester Co., Chicago, Ill.	4 gold-filled medals of honor	Trip to National 4-H Club Congress	None	6 scholarships of $500 each.
3. Automotive	The Firestone Tire & Rubber Co., Akron, Ohio	4 key chains	Trip to National 4-H Club Congress	None	6 scholarships of $500 each.
4. Beef	E. I. du Pont de Nemours & Co., Inc. Wilmington, Del.	4 gold-filled medals of honor	Trip to National 4-H Club Congress	None	6 scholarships of $500 each.
5. Bread	Standard Brands Inc., N.Y., N.Y.	4 gold-filled medals of honor	Trip to National 4-H Club Congress	None	6 scholarships of $500 each.
6. Clothing	Coats & Clark, Inc., New York, N.Y.	4 gold-filled medals of honor	Trip to National 4-H Club Congress	None	12 scholarships of $500 each.
7. Conservation of Natural Resources	John Deere Moline, Ill.	4 gold-filled medals of honor	Trip to National 4-H Club Congress	None	6 scholarships of $500 each.
8. Dairy	Oliver Corporation Chicago, Ill.	4 gold-filled medals of honor	Trip to National 4-H Club Congress	None	6 scholarships of $500 each.
9. Dairy Foods	Carnation Company Los Angeles, Calif.	4 gold-filled medals of honor	wrist watch to state winner	18 trips to National 4-H Club Congress	6 scholarships of $500 each.
10. Dog Care & Training	Ralston Purina Co. St. Louis, Mo.	4 gold-filled medals of honor	Wrist watch	None	10 trips to National 4-H Club Congress

43 Silver tray awards given by the President of the United States.

Awards Program	Donor	County	State	Sectional	National
11. Dress Revue	Simplicity Pattern Co. Inc., N.Y., N.Y.	gold-shaded medals to the blue group	Trip to National 4-H Club Congress	None	Leather-cased scissors to state winner
12. Electric	Westinghouse Educational Foundation, Pittsburg, Pa.	4 gold-filled medals of honor	Trip to National 4-H Club Congress Plaque to one county	None	6 scholarships of $500 each.
13. Entomology	Hercules Powder Co. Wilmington, Del.	4 gold-filled medals of honor	Trip to National 4-H Club Congress	None	6 scholarships of $500 each.
14. Field Crops	Arcadian Products Dept., Allied Chemical Corp., New York, N.Y.	4 gold-filled medals of honor	Trip to National 4-H Club Congress	None	6 scholarships of $500 each.
15. Foods-Nutrition	General Foods Corporation, White Plains, N.Y.	4 gold-filled medals of honor	Trip to National 4-H Club Congress	None	6 scholarships of $500 each.
16. Food Preservation	Kerr Glass Mf. Corp. Sand Springs, Okla.	4 gold-filled medals of honor	Trip to National 4-H Club Congress	None	6 scholarships of $500 each.
17. Forestry	American Forest Products Industries Inc. Washington, D.C.	4 gold-filled medals of honor	Fountain pen & pencil set	12 trips to National 4-H Club Congress	6 scholarships of $500 each.
18. Garden	Allis-Chalmers Mfg. Co., Milwaukee, Wis.	4 gold-filled medals of honor	Trip to National 4-H Club Congress	None	8 scholarships of $500 each.
19. Health	Eli Lilly & Co. Indianapolis, Ind.	4 gold-filled medals Certificates to 4 clubs	Trip to National 4-H Club Congress Certificates to 10 clubs	None	6 scholarships of $500 each.
20. Home Economics	Montgomery Ward Chicago, Ill.	4 gold-filled medals of honor	Trip to National 4-H Club Congress	None	6 scholarships of $500 each.
21. Home Improvement	Hutchinson Co., New York, N.Y.	4 gold-filled medals of honor	Trip to National 4-H Club Congress	None	6 scholarships of $500 each.

Awards Program	Donor	County	State	Sectional	National
22. Leadership	The Sears-Roebuck Foundation, Chicago, Ill.	4 gold-filled medals of honor	Trip to National 4-H Club Congress	None	12 scholarships of $500 each.
23. Photography	Eastman Kodak Co Rochester, N.Y.	4 gold-filled medals of honor	$25 U.S. Savings Bond	None	None
24. Poultry	Heisdorf & Nelson Farms, Inc. Kirkland, Wash.	4 gold-filled medals of honor	Trip to National 4-H Club Congress	None	scholarships of $500 each.
25. Safety	General Motors Detroit, Mich.	4 gold-filled medals of honor Certificates to 4 clubs	Trip to National 4-H Club Congress Certificates to 10 clubs Plaque to one county	None	8 scholarships of $500 each.
26. Swine	Moorman Mfg. Co. Quincy, Ill.	4 gold-filled medals of honor	Trip to National 4-H Club Congress	None	6 scholarships of $500 each.
27. Tractor	American Oil Foundation; Humble Oil & Refining Co.; Standard Oil Co. (Ky.) Standard Oil Co. (Ohio)	4 gold-filled medals of honor 4 gold-filled medals of honor	Trip to National 4-H Club Congress Trip to National 4-H Club Congress	None	12 scholarships of $500 each.
28. Special Programs					
A.	Citizenship Friends of Thomas E. Wilson	None	Certificate of honor (one for boy & one for girl)	None	2 trips to National 4-H Club Congress & 2 $500 scholarships. Silver trays (boy & girl).
B.	Public Speaking The Pure Oil Co. Palatine, Ill.	Two gold-filled medals of honor	Wrist watch for boy & chest of silverware for girl	None	2 trips to National 4-H Club Congress & 2 scholarships of $500 each.
C.	Crop Protection Calif. Chemical Co., Ortho Div. San Francisco, Calif.	None	None	None	2 scholarships of $800 each.

County & State Awards offered in 2 states

College Scholarship Fund

Awards Program	Donor	County	State	Sectional	National
D. Home Economics	Sunbeam Corp. Chicago 50, Ill. The Sperry & Hutchinson Co. New York, N.Y.; Pyrofax Gas Corporation New York, 17, N.Y.; The West Bend Company, West Bend, Wis.	None	None	None	2 $800 scholarships 2 $800 scholarships 3 $500 scholarships 2 $800 scholarships
E. Forestry	Homelife, a division of Textron Inc., Port Chester, N.Y.	None	None	None	4 scholarships of $1600 each.
F. Sheep	Wilson & Co. Inc. Chicago, Ill.	None	None	None	6 scholarships of $500 each.
Awards for Former 4-H Members:					
29. Alumni Recognition	Olin Mathieson Corp. New York, N.Y.	4 gold-filled recognition pins	4 recognition plaques	None	8 gold keys and trips to National 4-H Club Congress

DURATION OF SPONSORSHIP UP TO 1964

Program	Donor	Years Sponsored	Additional Years Other Programs Sponsored	Scholarships Awarded in 1964
Achievement	Ford Motor Co. Fund	3	10	12
Agriculture	International Harvester Co.	10	30	6
Automotive	Firestone Tire & Rubber Co.	5	16	6
Beef	E.I. du Pont de Nemours & Co.	6	--	6
Clothing	Coats & Clark	24	--	12
Conservation of Natural Resources	John Deere	1	4	6
Dairy	Oliver Corp.	13	--	6
Dress Revue	Simplicity Pattern Co., Inc.	18	--	--
Electric	Westinghouse Elec. Corp.	29	--	6
Entomology	Hercules Powder Co.	13	--	6
Field Crops	Arcadian Products Dept. Allied Chem. Corp.	8	--	6
Foods–Nutrition	General Foods Corp.	4	--	6
Food Preservation	Kerr Glass Mfg. Corp.	36	--	6
Garden	Allis Chalmers Mfg. Co.	19	--	8
Health	Eli Lilly & Co.	9	--	6
Home Economics	Montgomery Ward	42	--	6
Home Improvement	The S & H Foundation, Inc. (Sperry & Hutchinson)	3	--	6
Leadership	Sears-Roebuck Foundation	4	36	12
Poultry	Heisdorf & Nelson Farms, Inc.	3	--	6
Safety	General Motors	20	--	6
Swine	Moormen Mfg. Co.	7	--	6
Tractor	American Oil Foundation; Humble Oil Refining; Standard Oil Co. Kentucky & Ohio	20	--	12 Sectional trips awarded in 1964
Dairy Foods	Carnation Co. (18 trips)	17	--	6

Program	Donor	Years Sponsored	Additional Years Other Programs Sponsored	Scholarships Awarded in 1964
Forestry	American Forest Prod. Indu- stries, Inc. (12 trips)	17	--	6
Sheep	Wilson & Co. (6 trips)	1	--	6
Dog Care & Training	Ralston Purina Co. (10 trips)	6	--	--
Citizenship	Memorial to Thomas E. Wilson (2 trips)	--	--	2
Photography	Eastman Kodak Co. (8 trips)	1	--	---
Alumni Recognition	Olin Mathieson Chemical Corp. (8 trips)	12	9	8

State Sponsored Trips Missouri

Program	Donor	Years Sponsored		
Public Speaking	Southwestern Bell Telephone Company (2 trips)	11		
Meat Animal	Missouri Produc- tion Live- stock Mar- keting Associations: St. Louis, Kansas City, & St. Joseph (1 trip)	25		

FORMER NATIONAL AWARD SPONSORS

1938-1962	Beautification of Home Grounds	Mrs. Charles R. Walgreen
1934-1957	Meat Animal	Thomas E. Wilson
1947-1959	Leadership	Edward Foss Wilson
1935-1950	Food Preparation	Servel, Inc.
1941-1948	Dairy Foods Demonstrations	Kraft Foods
1947-1955	Health	Kellogg
1948-1956	Recreation	U.S. Tire & Rubber Co.
1933-1943	Dress Revue	Chicago Mail Order
1956-1960	Frozen Foods	Whirlpool Corporation
1950-1955	Community Relations	Wm. Wrigly & Gene Autry

Both Armour and Swift Packing Companies have provided various sponsored programs through the years to the 4-H Club Congress, or related projects.

The Rock Island, Chicago, Milwaukee and St. Paul Railroads have made annual con- tributions to the program over a long period of time.

MISSOURI WINNERS OF NATIONAL 4-H SCHOLARSHIPS TO 1964

Year	Name	County	Program
1931	E. C. Adams, Jr.	Jackson	($500) I-H
	Doris M. Hostetter	Jackson	($500) I-H
	John Batt	Worth	($500) I-H
1941	Margery Hableutzel	Buchanan	Leadership ($300)
1945	Estelle Stewart	Mercer	Achievement
1946	Estelle Stewart	Mercer	Leadership ($200)
	Shirley Peterman	Saline	Electricity ($200)
1948	James Sutherland	Johnson	Electricity ($200)
	Paula Costley	Jasper	Clothing ($200)
	Nelson Perrey	Osage	Safety ($200)
	Dorothy McCue	Andrew	Girl's Record ($200)
	James T. Davis	Harrison	Soil Conservation ($200)
	Carolyn Vandiver	Shelby	Home Grounds ($200)
1949	Rosalie Powell	New Madrid	Girl's Record ($200)
	Emelia Ryan	Andrew	Home Improvement ($300)
	Dorothy McCue	Andrew	Achievement ($300)
1951	Clark Garner	Shelby	Home Improvement ($300)
1952	Bernice Roach	Nodaway	Health ($100)
	Marlene Preacher	Linn	Food Preparation ($300)
1953	Don McCool	Clinton	Poultry ($300)
	Nellie L. Osborn	Dunklin	Garden ($300)
	Pat Coppersmith	Nodaway	Health ($100)
	Keith Boyer	Scotland	Leadership ($150)
	Norma Homefield	Lafayette	AT&SF ($250)
	Kendal Anderson	Cass	Cattle Judging ($300)
	Junior Boyer	Scotland	AT&SF ($250)
1954	Phyllis Schuesing	Pettis	Clothing ($300)
	Billie Joe West	Platte	West Animal ($300)
	Donald Estep	Andrew	Achievement ($300)
	Jo Ann Washburn	Linn	AT&SF ($250)
	Donald Estep	Andrew	AT&SF ($250)
1955	Marilyn Maize	Harrison	Achievement ($300)
	Marvin Hagen	Nodaway	Recreation ($300)
	Rodney Garnett	Cole	Achievement ($300)
	Martha Ann Davis	Harrison	Girl's Record ($300)
	Kathleen Moore	Shelby	AT&SF ($250)
	George Barnitz	Dent	AT&SF ($250)
1956	James R. Teegarden	Caldwell	Achievement ($300)
	Joan Washburn	Linn	Achievement ($300)
	Edwin S. Turner	Buchanan	Forestry ($300)
	James Sprake	Buchanan	AT&SF ($200)
	Georgia Hughes	Cedar	AT&SF ($200)
1957	Ronald Powell	Randolph	Safety ($400)
	Edward Polovich	Adair	Electricity ($400)
	Geneva K. Helwig	Callaway	Clothing ($400)
	James O. Chest	Andrew	AT&SF ($250)
	Bob Bail	Cooper	AT&SF ($250)
1958	Helen Mongler	Adrain	Clothing ($400)
	Gary Clarkson	Macon	Tractor ($400)
	Judith Wood	Shelby	Home Economics ($400)
	Charles Keller	Marion	Soil Conservation ($400)
	Gail Buchett	Adair	AT&SF ($350)
	Mary Joan Temple	Lafayette	AT&SF ($350)

Year	Name	County	Program
1959	Gloria Rickhof	Lafayette	Clothing ($400)
	Janet Winn	Randolph	Dairy ($400)
	Harlan Borman	Callaway	Dairy ($400)
	Leona Santeer	Barry	AT&SF ($350)
	Robert Findley	St. Louis	AT&SF ($350)
1960	Donald Rogers	Adair	Agriculture ($400)
	Judith Stonner	Saline	Bread ($400)
	Aleta Van Leave	Macon	Canning ($400)
	Donnie Yoest	Moniteau	Electricity ($400)
	Marie K. May	Franklin	Health ($400)
	Frances McQueen	Holt	Leadership ($400)
	Joan Turner	Buchanan	AT&SF ($400)
	Leroy Hurr	Scotland	AT&SF ($400)
	Mary Ellen McClurg	Lawrence	AT&SF ($400)
1961	Charnett Norton	Clinton	Bread ($400)
	Harold Storck	Barry	Dairy ($400)
	Lawrence Meyer	Nodaway	Tractor ($400)
	Robert Horton	Adair	AT&SF ($400)
	Mary Ellen McClurg	Lawrence	AT&SF ($400)
1962	Deanna Akers	Stoddard	Clothing ($400)
	Jean Harris	Clinton	Food and Nutrition ($400)
	Julia Schmidt	Franklin	Recreation ($400)
	Kathleen McKenzie	Knox	Poultry ($400)
	Marian Zularf	Greene	AT&SF ($400)
	Leon McIntyre	Nodaway	AT&SF ($400)
1963	Rebecca L. Hargers	Atchison	Canning ($500)
	Phillip F. Hanson	Pike	Health ($500)
	Barbara Frieling	Marion	AT&SF ($400)
	Bill Schabbing	Cape Girardeau	AT&SF ($400)
1964	Vera Jane Holtkamp	Audrain	Health ($500)
	Ron Davis	Audrain	Field Crops ($500)
	Lola Barnett	Christian	AT&SF ($500)
	Allan Smith	Vernon	AT&SF ($500)

OFFICERS OF MISSOURI 4-H CLUB COUNCIL

Officers	County
1946-47	
Herbert Clizer, President	Andrew
Margaret Palmer, Vice-President	Randolph
Don Hollingsworth, Secretary	Buchanan
1947-48	
Ralph Hays, President	Pemiscot
Eldon Leiter, Vice-President	Pettis
Mary Frances Stewart, Secretary	Jackson
1948-49	
George Jones, President	Macon
Wayne Gerber, Vice-President	Andrew
Alice Englebrecht, Secretary	Cole
1949-50	
Emmett Fairfax, President	Pettis
Don Rutter, Vice-President	Shelby
Dorothea McCue, Secretary	Andrew
Rita Pittman, Treasurer	Dunklin
1950-51	
Don Rutter, President	Shelby
Rita Pittman, Vice-President	Dunklin
Marjorie Nold, Secretary	Andrew
Mary Jones, Treasurer	Macon
1951-52	
Arthur Kelly, President	Jackson
Bob Baker, Vice-President	Johnson
Joan Phillips, Secretary	Livingston
Leroy Englebrecht, Treasurer	Cole
1952-53	
Johnny Gibbens, President	Buchanan
Frank Davis, Vice-President	Harrison
Sandra Harlans, Secretary	Jackson
Jack Whitesell, Treasurer	Cedar
1953-54	
Carrol Switzer, President	Linn
Jack Whitesell, Vice-President	Cedar
Jeanice Harbold, Secretary	New Madrid
Mary Lister, Treasurer	Cole
1954-55	
Durward Morre, President	Gasconade
Eddie Crouch, Vice-President	Clay
Pat Copperfield, Secretary	Nodaway
Rodney Garnett, Treasurer	Cole
1955-56	
Konrad Heid, President	Cass
Marilyn Marsh, Vice-President	Texas
Junita Snider, Secretary	Platte
Earlene Christianson, Treasurer	Bates
1956-57	
Billy Joe West, President	Platte

Officers	County
Bryon Simpson, Vice-President	Clinton
Martha Davis, Secretary	Harrison
Joe Pendergrast, Treasurer	Jasper

1958-59

Robert Fridley, President	St. Louis
Lynn Ballew, Vice-President	Jackson
Shirley Ann Edwards, Secretary	Audrain
Doris Storck, Treasurer	Barry

1959-60

Jerry Goos, President	Lincoln
Ann Utterback, Vice-President	Ralls
Mary Myers, Secretary	Ray
Pat McLarney, Treasurer	Clinton

1960-61

John Crouch, President	Clay
Quinten Huss, Vice-President	Clinton (deceased)
Bonnie Shirley, Secretary	Carroll
Larry Sanders, Treasurer	Jasper

1961-62

Addrell Davison, President	Adair
Leona Santee, Vice-President	Barry
Vida Loberg, Secretary	Cape Girardeau
Bob Horton, Treasurer	Adair

1962-63

Franklin Wallace, President	Iron
Don Bollinger, Vice-President	Scott
Peggy Overton, Secretary	Grundy
Deanna Akers, Treasurer	Stoddard

1963-64

Don Chapman, Pres dent	Lawrence
Jerri Hammond, Vice-President	Grundy
Dawn Poole, Secretary	Sullivan
Patricia Minks, Treasurer	Franklin

1964-65

Charles Humphreys, President	Saline
Ralph Gates, Vice-President	Knox
Cathie Weihe, Secretary	Platte
Carmen Pope, Treasurer	St. Francois

1952 COMMUNITY 4-H LEADERS' CAMPS

(This 1952 schedule provides a sample of yearly leader training camp conferences.)

Name	Location	Date	No. Ldrs. & Agents Attending	No. Years Camp	Sponsors
Frenchman's Bluff	Cuiver River	May 20–22	66	2	Producers Livestock Marketing Ass'n, Nat. Stock Yards Ill.
Union Electric Co.	Valley Park	June 30–July 2	89	3 3	Union Electric Co., St. Louis
Clover Point	Lake of Ozark State Park	July 27–29	96	4	Gulf, Mobile & Ohio R.R. Co.
Ginger Blue	Noel	Sept. 4–6	78	1	Empire Dist. Electric Co. Thurston Chemical Company, Joplin
Bob White	Knobnoster State Park	Sept. 11–17	54	3	Iowa–Mo. Walnut Co., St. Joseph Light & Power Co., Dannen Mills, St. Joseph
Clover Point	Lake of Ozark	Sept. 29–Oct. 1	65	1	Mo. Chain Store Council (W.F.)
Big Springs	Van Buren State Park	Oct. 2–4	65	1	Ark–Mo Power Co. Blytheville, Ark.
TOTAL	8 Camps		569		